Land Warfare: Brassey
Weapons Systems and 1

RADAR

Land Warfare:
Brassey's New Battlefield Weapons Systems and Technology Series

Executive Editor: Colonel R G Lee OBE, Former Military Director of Studies, Royal Military College of Science, Shrivenham, UK

Editor-in-Chief: Professor Frank Hartley, Vice Chancellor, Cranfield Institute of Technology, UK

The success of the first series on Battlefield Weapons Systems and Technology and the pace of advances in military technology have prompted Brassey's to produce a new Land Warfare series. This series updates subjects covered in the original series and also covers completely new areas. The books are written for military personnel who wish to advance their professional knowledge. In addition, they are intended to aid anyone who is interested in the design, development and production of military equipment.

Volume 1 Guided Weapons — R G Lee *et al.*

Volume 2 Explosives, Propellants and Pyrotechnics — A Bailey and S G Murray

Volume 3 Noise in the Military Environment — R F Powell and M R Forrest

Volume 4 Ammunition — P R Courtney-Green

Volume 5 Communications and Information Systems for Battlefield Command and Control — M A Rice and A J Sammes

Volume 6 Military Helicopters — E J Everett-Heath, G M Moss, A W Mowat and K E Reid

Volume 7 Fighting Vehicles — T W Terry *et al.*

Volume 8 Surveillance and Target Acquisition Systems — A C Figgures *et al.*

Volume 9 Radar — P S Hall *et al.*

For full details of titles in this series, please contact your local Brassey's Pergamon office.

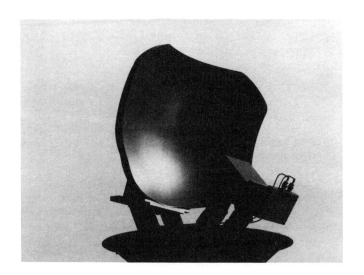

RADAR

P. S. Hall

T. K. Garland-Collins

R. S. Picton

R. G. Lee

Royal Military College of Science, Shrivenham, UK

BRASSEY'S (UK)

Member of the Maxwell Macmillan Pergamon Publishing Corporation

LONDON · OXFORD · WASHINGTON · NEW YORK · BEIJING
FRANKFURT · SÃO PAULO · SYDNEY · TOKYO · TORONTO

U.K. (Editorial)	Brassey's (UK) Ltd., 50 Fetter Lane, London EC4A 1AA, England
(Orders)	Brassey's (UK) Ltd., Headington Hill Hall, Oxford OX3 0BW, England
U.S.A. (Editorial)	Brassey's (US) Inc., 8000 Westpark Drive, Fourth Floor, McLean, Virginia 22102, U.S.A.
(Orders)	Pergamon Press, Inc., Maxwell House, Fairview Park, Elmsford, New York 10523, U.S.A.
PEOPLE'S REPUBLIC OF CHINA	Pergamon Press, Room 4037, Qianmen Hotel, Beijing, People's Republic of China
GERMANY	Pergamon Press GmbH, Hammerweg 6, D-6242 Kronberg, Germany
BRAZIL	Pergamon Editora Ltda, Rua Eça de Queiros, 346, CEP 04011, Paraiso, São Paulo, Brazil
AUSTRALIA	Brassey's (Australia) Pty Ltd., P.O. Box 544, Potts Point, N.S.W. 2011, Australia
JAPAN	Pergamon Press Ltd., 5th Floor, Matsuoka Central Building, 1-7-1 Nishishinjuku, Shinjuku-ku, Tokyo 160, Japan
CANADA	Pergamon Press Canada Ltd., Suite No. 271, 253 College Street, Toronto, Ontario, Canada M5T 1R5

Copyright © 1991 Brassey's (UK)

First edition 1991

Library of Congress Cataloging in Publication Data
Radar/P. S. Hall . . . [et al.].—1st ed.
p.   cm.—(Land warfare; v. **9**)
1. Radar—Military applications.   I. Hall, P. S. (Peter S.)
II. Series.
UG612.R33   1991   623'.7348—dc20   90–20493

British Library Cataloguing in Publication Data
Radar
1. Radar
I. Hall, P. S. (Peter S.)   II. Series
621.3848

ISBN 0–08–037710–6 (Hardcover)
ISBN 0–08–037711–4 (Flexicover)

Front cover photo: Patriot Air Defence Radar System
(*Courtesy Raytheon*)

Printed in Great Britain by BPCC Wheatons Ltd., Exeter

Preface

This Series

This series of books is written for those who wish to improve their knowledge of military weapons and equipment. It is equally relevant to professional soldiers, those involved in developing or producing military weapons or indeed anyone interested in the art of modern warfare.

All the texts are written in a way which assumes no mathematical knowledge and no more technical depth than would be gleaned by any person who keeps himself or herself informed of developments in the modern world. It is intended that the books should be of particular interest to officers in the Armed Services wishing to further their professional knowledge as well as anyone involved in research, development, production, testing and maintenance of defence equipments.

The principal authors of the books are all members of the staff of the Royal Military College of Science, Shrivenham, which is composed of a unique blend of academic and military experts. They are not only leaders in the technology of their subjects, but are aware of what the military practitioner needs to know. It is difficult to imagine any group of persons more fitted to write about the application of technology to the battlefield.

This Volume

Since Sir Robert Watson-Watt first demonstrated a 'Radio Locating System' in 1935, the development of radar has surged forward at an urgent rate which, as yet, shows no sign of abating. In the first wartime years of its use, it was a most useful detection system and was a vital element in deciding the outcome of the Battle of Britain. As time has passed it has become an even more important component of weapon systems and tactics. It is to be found in elements of battlefield Command and Control from AWACS to hand-held battlefield radars and as a component part of many Guided Weapon systems. Indeed it is now impossible to plan a modern battle, on land, sea or in the air, without due regard to the winning of the Electronic Warfare element of it. A study of wars in the past two decades will highlight the battle winning status of the Electronic Warfare duel: and it is mainly about radar. This volume is intended to give the informed, but not necessarily technically expert, reader, a wide view of the way radar works, is developing and is used. It should provide those for whom radar is their main subject, with a useful overview prior to delving more deeply into the aspects of particular interest to them; it should be sufficient by itself for those who need to know about radar as part of their work.

17 August 1990

FRANK HARTLEY
GEOFFREY LEE

Contents

List of Illustrations

Chapter 4—Radar Technology

Chapter 5—Battlefield Surveillance Radar

Chapter 6—Weapon Locating Radars

Chapter 7—Air Defence Radar

Chapter 8—Other Battlefield Radars

Chapter 9—Electronic Warfare

Chapter 10—Conclusions

List of Tables

1

Introduction to Radar

The Importance of Radar

The term radar is derived from the description of its first primary role as a *ra*dio *de*tection *a*nd *r*anging system. It was originally devised as a means of detecting approaching aircraft at long range to enable defences to react in sufficient time to counter the threat. The ability to measure the range and target direction were additional advantages allowing improved defensive deployment. The major technical advances that have since taken place make radar an important part of the overall surveillance and target acquisition field. Its key properties are that it can detect many small, fast targets at long ranges, day or night, through cloud, dust or battlefield obscuration. However, radar is an active system emitting electromagnetic energy and its resolution is poor when compared to electro-optic devices. Nevertheless, its significant advantages make it the best solution in some of the more demanding military tasks such as gun location and air defence.

The Origin and Development of Military Radars

Pre-war Developments

The military need for some form of target detection to improve on the performance of the human eye was first recognised in 1917, when German aircraft and *Zeppelin*s began to attack cities in England. The British Army's reaction was to withdraw searchlights from the coastal defence role, in which they were used to sweep the surface of the water, to the cities, where they were later supplemented by coarse sound locators. Air defence (AD) remained the main driving force behind the development of detection systems for a further two decades. The state of the art at that time made radio detection impractical, so the Air Defence Experimental Establishment, set up in 1922 at Biggin Hill, concentrated on sound location. The result was acoustic mirrors and Figure 1.1 shows an example. Mirrors were also used in Malta. In the 1930s the threat of war and, in particular, the menace of the burgeoning *Luftwaffe*, spurred efforts to find an answer to the aircraft detection requirement. In 1935 the Daventry experiment, described later in this chapter, gave birth to the age of radio detection and made the mirror a gravestone of acoustic development.

Radar Comes of Age

Within two years of that momentous experiment a radar system with a range of 40 miles against a bomber aircraft was available and in 1940, in time to play its

FIG. 1.1   Acoustic mirror for sound location of aircraft *(Courtesy Imperial War Museum)*

decisive role in the Battle of Britain, a radar chain, the Home Chain system, was in place on the east and southeast coasts. The Germans had also developed radar in roughly the same time frame and to a similar operational capability. The British, driven by the need to defend their homeland, had gone further and produced a remarkably effective co-ordinated radar system. As the war progressed this Home Chain system was improved and by 1942 it was using the now familiar rotating antennas. Meanwhile, in 1940, the magnetron was invented. This allowed the use of much shorter wavelengths and consequently gave much improved definition. It was this which probably changed the outcome of the Battle of the Atlantic through the ability it sired to detect U boats. The magnetron was a rare example of a piece of technology developed by one side and not the other.

First Uses in Armies

As the power problem was solved and the size of components was reduced, so radar was introduced increasingly into aircraft and ships. Today there are few airborne or seaborne weapon systems which do not have a radar heart. Army air defence and coastal defence units also used radar, but it was only as the wavelength reduced and missiles were developed, in the decades after the war, that armies adopted it to any considerable extent.

Air Defence

The characteristics of radar are long range, the ability to see through smoke, fog and rain, and a capability to measure range and speed. These are all well suited to the original radar role of AD. Coupled into AD systems we now find radars in the following roles:

Surveillance—variously known as search, acquisition and tactical control.
Tracking—fire control or target illumination.

First, and still used in conjunction with AD guns, they are now more widely found in surface-to-air missile (SAM) systems.

Battlefield Surveillance

The sea and air provide easier backgrounds against which to use radar than the cluttered earth. More will be explained about this later. Nevertheless, battlefield surveillance radars (BSR) have been developed and in service for the past 20 years. Although not taken into service, the *Shrimp* radar, shown in Figure 1.2, gives a

FIG. 1.2 *Shrimp*, a short range battlefield surveillance radar *(Courtesy G. Lee)*

good impression of the small size that can be achieved. In this manportable environment, size and weight are paramount. Displays that can be easily interpreted are essential, too, if operator training and operation are to be simple. The restricted intervisibility at ground level has been a severe limiting factor: in Europe it is rarely possible to see more than 6–15 km. Consequently, much investigation has been made into methods of elevating the radars. Raised platforms, tethered platforms, helicopters and fixed wing aircraft have all been impressed into service, but enemy electronic counter measures, aircraft vulnerability, cost, complexity, ground obscuration and difficulties of concealment all create problems in this role. Currently, emphasis is being placed on systems that can reach out to a depth of about 150 km behind the enemy forward troops from their mountings in fixed wing aircraft flying over friendly territory. The cluttered earth remains a difficult radar environment.

Weapon Locating

Counter-bombardment has always been a prime requirement of the army. The problem has been to locate the artillery that was to be counter-bombarded. For many decades sound-ranging has been used, but more recently radar locating techniques have entered service. Figure 1.3 shows the principles. The flat

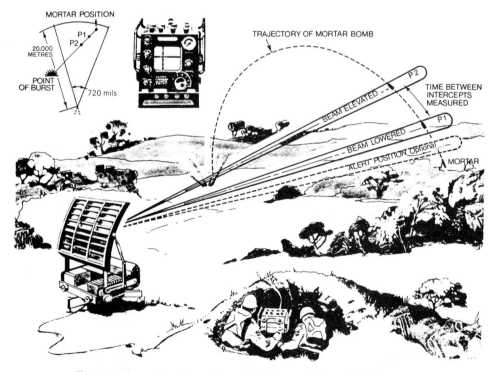

FIG. 1.3   Weapon location using radar *(Courtesy Thorn EMI Electronics)*

horizontal beam maintains an alert position just above the horizon. When a projectile passes through it, the radar head is lifted twice, ahead of it. From these two detections the system computes the range and velocity of the projectile and consequently its trajectory. Tracing back the trajectory gives the position of the weapon. The characteristics of the target determine the ease of its detection: the larger its surface area, the greater the reflectivity of the material from which it is made and the slower the velocity, the easier it is to detect. It is no coincidence that Figure 1.3 demonstrates the radar locating a mortar. The mortar bomb is slower and larger than a shell and the first generation of weapon locating radars have been restricted to the location of mortars. Now gun and rocket locating systems have been developed and are entering service.

Smart New Ideas

As the requirement for greater accuracy and discrimination has grown, so the wavelengths have crept down. Now millimetric wavelengths are possible and, in their turn, they permit much greater ability to discriminate between different types of target, even to the extent of coarse imaging. At the same time the radar equipment itself has reduced in size. This combination has made it feasible to put radar systems into the warheads of missiles and terminally guided sub-munitions (TGSM). The end result will be intelligent munitions which locate and select their own targets. Such smart ideas will determine the future of radar in the next two or three decades.

Technical History

The Invention of Radar

The technical history of radar starts as early as 1873 when Maxwell described in mathematical form how electromagnetic waves could propagate through the atmosphere. Soon after, in 1887, Hertz demonstrated it practically and the era of radio communications and radar was born. The actual concept of reflection of the wave off a body and hence of detection was first proposed by Tesla in 1900. The first patent and practical radar is credited to the German, Hulsmeyer, in 1904. His 'telemobiloscope' was designed as an anti-collision device for ships. He was no doubt spurred on in his work by observing the grief of a mother whose son was killed when two ships collided. Figure 1.4 shows his invention. Radio waves at

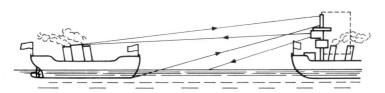

FIG. 1.4   Hulsmeyer's collision prevention radar, 1904

650 MHz were generated by a spark gap and focused by a parabolic reflector antenna located on the mast. The echo was picked up by a second receiving antenna also formed by a parabolic reflector. When a ship came within a certain distance a bell was automatically rung. The radar was continuous wave and not pulsed and the problem of distance measurement was overcome by pointing the antenna down towards the water. The waves would reflect off the surface and hit the target. The range could be calculated from the antenna angle and knowledge of its height above the water. Although successfully demonstrated at ranges of up to 3 km, neither government nor commerce took up the idea.

Primitive Advances

Between 1904 and 1935 many people around the world engaged in the radar field. Notable amongst these was Marconi, the pioneer of radio communication, who tried to encourage radar research, particularly in America. Radar devices were proposed in detail by Taylor and Young in the United States in 1922 and by Alder from the Royal Navy Signal School in England in 1928. During this time radar technology was primitive, although many of the principal components, described later, were available. For example, the cathode ray oscilloscope (CRO), used extensively to display radar signals, was invented in 1897 by Ferdinand Brown and by about 1930 industrial laboratories were producing compact CROs that were sensitive, reliable and moderately priced. In addition, low power magnetron transmitters, and superheterodyne receivers and parabolic antennas had all been developed and the Doppler principle was understood. It has been said that practical radar development was imminent by the beginning of the war and would have happened anyway, but it was the military need itself that spurred the rapid advances from 1930 onwards.

Detection of aircraft was first shown to be possible in 1930 by L. A. Hyland, working at the Naval Research Laboratory in the United States. Hyland was studying communications between a ground transmitter and an aircraft mounted antenna at 33 MHz by rotating the aircraft on a large turntable. His measurements were disturbed unaccountably and it was only when he noted the presence of aircraft flying across the communications line of sight that the application to aircraft detection was realised and the link with the earlier Taylor and Young 1922 proposal made. Further experiments followed and it was established that detection of aircraft as high as 8,000 ft and at 10 miles range was possible using this continuous wave system. Work continued and in 1934 R. M. Page, employing principles used in acoustic depth finding, developed the radar pulse method of target ranging. Pulses of about 10 μs (10 millionth of a second) could be generated. By 1935 a successful pulse radar was built and demonstrated out to ranges of 25 miles.

The Daventry Experiment

In 1935 R. A. Watson-Watt and A. F. Wilkins performed the historic demonstration of radar that has now become known as the Daventry experiment and that led to the rapid development of radar in Britain. Wilkins and Watson-

Watt had prepared a memorandum to the Air Ministry committee on air defence on the use of short wave electromagnetic radiation for detection of aircraft. The Air Member for Research and Development, Sir Hugh Dowding, was quoted as saying, 'You know these scientific blokes can prove anything by figures. I want a demonstration.' A demonstration was therefore arranged. The transmitting station at Daventry was chosen because it operated at 6 MHz. The Heyford bomber used for the demonstration had a wing span of about 25 m which was about half a wavelength at 6 MHz. Wilkins had assumed that an object of the same size as a half wave dipole would strongly reflect the radio waves. Figure 1.5 shows the

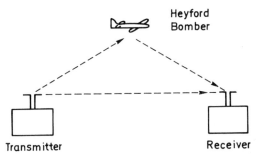

FIG. 1.5   The Daventry experiment, 1935

arrangement of the radar. A receiver was placed some way away from the transmitter. When the aircraft was flown through the main beam of the transmitting antenna the energy would be reflected down to the receiver. Any fluctuations caused by interference between the direct wave from the transmitter to the receiver and the reflected ray were displayed on a CRO. As the reflected ray would be smaller than the direct one, the antennas were adjusted to have minimum sensitivity along the ground, thus enhancing the interference effect. The arrangement is an example of a bistatic radar system in which, to obtain isolation between the very high transmitted power and very small received power, the two antennas are physically separated. (This concept is clarified later in this chapter and developments noted in subsequent chapters.)

The experiment was a success. The committee asked Watson-Watt to lead a six-strong development group on a budget of £12,300 for the first year, operating at Orfordness in Suffolk. Watson-Watt was previously superintendent of the Radio Research Station of the National Physical Laboratory at Slough. His great contribution to radar lies both in his administrative skill and willingness to give up his secure post at Slough and gamble his future on this new technology. It is interesting to note that Watson-Watt was not alone in proposing a radar system, at least two others being put forward during the war. One of these came from a schoolboy who, like Watson-Watt, had performed the theoretical calculations to estimate the possible range!

Radar into Action

The pace of radar development then quickened. The Chain Home system was built and installed along the east and south coasts of England to give early warning of approaching aircraft. Such was the desire for long range warning in the United Kingdom that the so-called 'Early Warning Chain' was planned in 1935 and the first chain station at Bawdsey Research Station in Suffolk was handed over to Royal Air Force personnel in early 1937. Many variants of the radar were made, ranging in frequency from 22 MHz to a few hundred megahertz, and uses ranged from that noted above to laying aids for searchlights and guns. Typical Chain Home towers are shown in Figure 1.6. The antennas were mounted on masts up to

FIG. 1.6 Chain Home radar aerials, Polney, Sussex *(Courtesy Imperial War Museum)*

350 ft high. The beamwidth on transmit was typically 60° in azimuth. The receive antennas had direction finding capabilities although errors of 10° were not uncommon. Mobile anti-aircraft radar developed in a similar way with the transmitter and receiver physically separate to form a bistatic system. Airborne radar was also developed for both airborne interception of aircraft (AI) and airborne detection of surface vessels (ASV).

In the United States radar development was centred at the Radiation Laboratories of the Massachusetts Institute of Technology with at one time over 4,000 staff. Nearly 150 distinct radar types were studied. The outcome in technical knowledge was immense and was later published in a 28-volume set known as the Research Laboratory Series. Some of the volumes remain as standard references today.

A Major Breakthrough

In parallel with this practical development, one example of an important breakthrough in component research should be mentioned. Following a visit to a

Chain Home station, workers at Birmingham University started work to improve various valves used in the radar. In 1940 Randall and Boot devised a new form of generating valve. Previous magnetrons were able to generate relatively low radio energy, typically a few hundred watts. Figure 1.7 shows the principle of the early

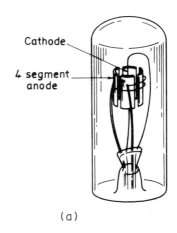

(a)

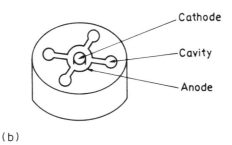

(b)

FIG. 1.7   Magnetron microwave generators: (a) split anode magnetron, (b) cavity magnetron

magnetron. A long wire cathode was made to glow and hence give off electrons. By applying a voltage between the cathode and anode the electrons move towards the cylindrical anode. This movement can be controlled by applying a magnetic field, generated by a large coil. The electron flow can be switched on and off, thus creating the action of a valve. If the valve is connected to a resonator circuit the combination will oscillate and produce power. However, external resonators absorb some of the power and this inefficiency limits power output. By designing an efficient cavity resonator within the magnetron, thus forming the 'cavity magnetron', Randall and Boot obtained very high pulse powers, typically many kilowatts. Figure 1.7b shows the original cathode surrounded by the anode which now consists of the original cylinder plus additional cylindrical cavities connected by slots. It is the diameter of the cavities that controls the frequency of oscillation.

This development significantly increased radar range and capability and paved the way for the subsequent huge growth in radar technology.

Since development of practical radars both in England and other countries during the Second World War, many new radar devices and techniques have been developed. The Doppler technique, understood prior to 1935, has now been extensively exploited to allow, for example, detection of small moving targets against a stationary background using the technique called moving target indication (MTI). Radar display technology has radically advanced. The advent of digital signal processing and phased array antennas has revolutionised radar capability. All these topics, in addition to radar fundamentals, are described in subsequent chapters.

Radar Types

There are two broad classes of radar relating, firstly, to the type of signal returning from the target and, secondly, to the relative position of the transmitter and receiver. In addition the position of radar frequency in the electromagnetic spectrum is a key classifier, particularly when relating it to other surveillance and target acquisition systems. These three classifications are discussed here. There are, of course, many other detailed classifications by technology and technique and these are explained throughout the book. All of these are additionally noted in the glossary of terms, together with other important radar nomenclature.

Primary and Secondary Radar

Figure 1.8 illustrates the difference between primary and secondary radars. In a primary radar the radar transmits a signal that hits the target, is reflected and travels back to the receiver. The target is detected by presence at the radar receiver of the reflected signal. Target direction is given by the antenna pointing angle and further information about the target such as range, speed or even type can be obtained by appropriate signal processing. In the secondary radar the transmitted signal is received by a transponder in the target. This then triggers a reply which is received by the radar. The reply can contain information about the target such as position, speed and target type. For example, in an airport control radar, the flight number is an important piece of information that could be established by a secondary radar. This type of radar is also known as a secondary surveillance radar (SSR) and relies on co-operation of the target to be successful. The degree of co-operation of the target can also be used to differentiate between a friendly and an enemy target and this forms the basis of identification friend or foe (IFF) systems.

Monostatic, Bistatic and Multistatic Radars

Figure 1.9 shows how the transmitter and receiver can be arranged to form monostatic, bistatic or multistatic radars. In a monostatic radar the transmitter and receiver are located in the same place and usually form the same piece of radar equipment. This allows the transmitter to be synchronised with the receiver and

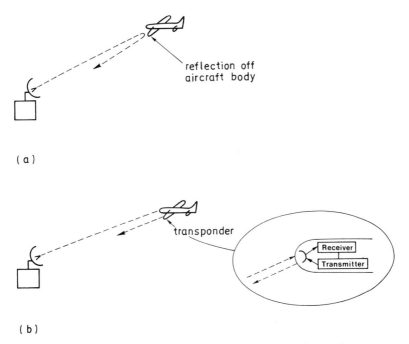

FIG. 1.8   Radar types: (a) primary radar, (b) secondary radar

the timing method used to measure target range is simple to implement. In a bistatic radar the transmitter and receiver are separated. As the receiver is purely passive it is less susceptile to some electronic countermeasures such as jamming and anti-radiation missiles. This is also the arrangement used in semi-active radar homing missiles, discussed in Chapter 8, where the transmitter is ground based and the receiver is in the missile nose. This simplifies the missile design and permits longer range operation.

Multistatic radar is an extension of the bistatic system where many widely spaced transmitters and receivers co-operate to form a sensor system that is highly capable and immune to countermeasures. Compared to monostatic and bistatic radars it is costly. The major technical problem in common with bistatic types is the need for synchronisation of the many elements.

The Electromagnetic Spectrum

Radar, in common with radio and electro-optic systems, uses electromagnetic energy. Figure 1.10 shows the electromagnetic frequency spectrum and indicates where these systems operate. The frequency scale is marked in hertz which was previously known as cycles per second. The wavelength scale is given in metres. The prefixes for both scales are explained in Table 1. The prefixes increase or decrease in factors of 10^3 or 1,000. The term tera is not often used. The term micrometre (μm) is widely used in the electro-optic field and is abbreviated to micron. Angstroms (Å) are also used for such equipment and are related to metres by 1 Å $= 10^{-10}$ m. Frequency f and wavelength λ are related by the velocity of light c

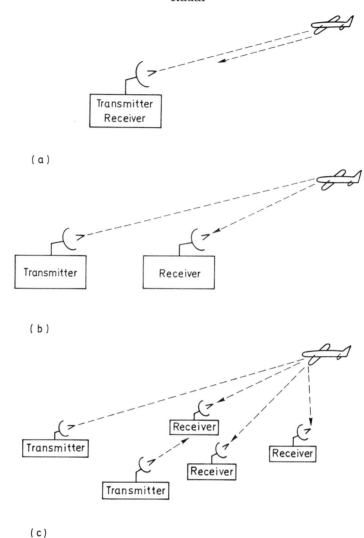

FIG. 1.9   Radar types: (a) monostatic radar, (b) bistatic radar, (c) multistatic radar

$$\lambda = c/f$$

where $c = 3 \times 10^8$ m/s.

The chart shows that radars currently operate over a wide range of frequencies from a few megahertz to over 100 GHz and share part of this range with communication systems. Electro-optic systems, on the other hand, work in the infra-red and visible range at frequencies that are very much higher than radar. As a consequence of this, these two forms of surveillance system have widely differing capabilities. In general terms, radar has poor resolution but works at long range in all weather, whereas electro-optic equipment has high resolution but only a short range, clear weather capability. These aspects are discussed further in Chapters 2 and 10.

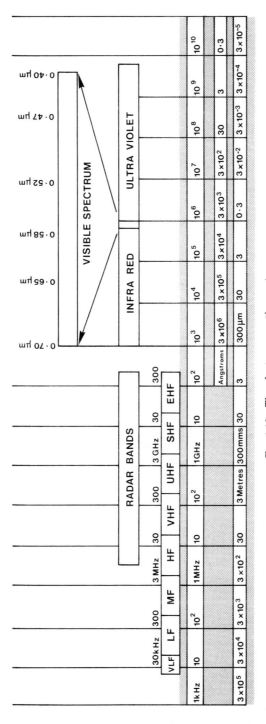

FIG. 1.10   The electromagnetic spectrum

TABLE 1.1

Prefixes used for Large and Small Numbers

Prefix	Meaning	Prefix	Meaning
k (kilo)	10^3	m (milli)	10^{-3}
M (mega)	10^6	μ (micro)	10^{-6}
G (giga)	10^9		
T (tera)	10^{12}		

TABLE 1.2

Radar Band Designations

Old radar bands Band	Frequency (GHz)	NATO bands Band	Frequency (GHz)
P	.225–1	A	up to .25
L	1–2	B	.25–.5
S	2–4	C	.5–1
C	4–8	D	1–2
X	8–12	E	2–3
J(Ku)	12–18	F	3–4
K	18–27	G	4–6
Q(Ka)	27–40	H	6–18
V	40–60	I	8–10
O(E)	60–90	J	10–20
		K	20–40
		L	40–60
		M	60–100

To aid frequency specification the radar bands are designated by letters. Table 2 shows the band ranges for both the old and new NATO designations.

Outline of Book Contents

This book is arranged in two distinct parts. Chapters 2 to 4 deal with radar principles and technology whilst Chapters 5 to 9 describe the application of radar to battlefield systems. Readers experienced in applications but who wish to strengthen their grasp of the fundamentals should study Chapters 2 to 4 whilst those who understand the basic action but who wish to update themselves on the current state of battlefield radars will find Chapters 5 to 9 useful. Of course for a full appreciation of applications, an understanding of the basics is necessary and for those new to the field or those wanting a comprehensive view we recommend working through the whole book.

To help readers deal with the difficult problem of nomenclature and terminology a glossary is included at the end of the book.

2

Principles of Radar Operation

The Radar Task

Radar operation is based on a number of simple principles that have been developed and expanded over the years to produce the sophisticated equipment described in the later chapters. In very basic terms the radar performs the following tasks:

- Detection of targets by sensing the tiny returning radio echo.
- Determination of target range by measuring the time taken for radiated pulses of electromagnetic waves to go to and return from the target.
- Location of the target direction by forming the waves into a narrow beam by use of a suitable antenna so that the direction in which the antenna points gives the target direction.
- Assessment of target velocity by measuring the change in frequency between the transmitted and received waves, the so-called Doppler effect.

Most modern radars have these features, although the specific application of each technique depends on the intended radar use. In addition, radars can build up further information about the target. For example, techniques exist to examine the target behaviour over a period of time, to create an image of the target, to record the way the target echo changes with time or to measure the echo polarisation. Measurement of target characteristics in such ways is an important aspect of current radar systems design. It allows, for example, air defence weapon control radars to possess automatic threat assessment capability, a crucial factor in rapid engagements. As another example, it can allow radar homing seekers in munitions to select optimum aiming points on ground targets to maximise kill probability. The improvement of existing methods, and the search for new ways to locate and identify targets, occupies an increasing part of today's radar designer's task.

In this chapter on the principles of radar, pulse radar action is described. In Chapter 3 Doppler radars are explained, together with other important techniques.

Pulse Radar Operation

Basic Action

The principles of a basic pulse radar are illustrated in Figure 2.1 which can be understood by considering the sequence of events that occur during operation:

- First, the clock instructs the oscillator to generate a short, high energy pulse at the radar frequency. As an example this pulse may have a duration τ of 1 μs (10^{-6} s) and will have a radar frequency of say 15 GHz for short range surveillance radar.

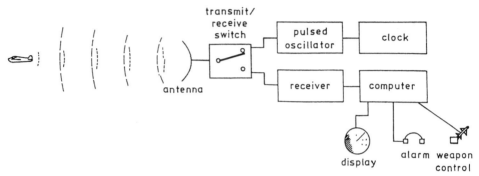

FIG. 2.1   Outline of simple pulse radar

- Whilst the pulse is generated the transmit/receive switch connects the oscillator to the antenna so that the energy can be radiated. The switch also serves to disconnect the receiver so that the high transmit power, which may be of the order of 10 kW (10^4 W) does not burn out the sensitive detector. This switching operation is known as duplexing.
- The radar energy travels to the target and is reflected back to the antenna. If the target range is R metres then the outward and return time in seconds is $t = 2R/c$ where c is the velocity of light (3×10^8 m/s). Thus for a 15 km range t is given by:

$$t = 2 \times 15 \times 10^3 / 3 \times 10^8 = 10^{-4}\text{ s or 100 }\mu\text{s}.$$

- After the pulse leaves the radar the transmit/receive switch connects the antenna to the receiver so that the return pulse can be detected. The return pulse power is very low compared to the transmitted power and may be 10^{-10} watts or less. The pulse time t is so short that it must be measured electronically. This can be done by use of a CRO, but, more often, by counting the number of timing pulses generated by a fast, quartz controlled oscillator of the type used in digital watches. The number of pulses counted between the transmitted and received pulses is a direct measure of t.
- After measuring t the computer will then pass on the range information, together with any other relevant data such as the antenna direction and any decisions made. This information can go, for example, to a display, an alarm, or to control a weapon system.

Of course in reality there may be many targets at various distances from the radar and to sort out their ranges the concept of range gates is used. Here the timing circuits are arranged so that if an echo return is present within a given time span, the signal is stored in a device called a gate. The time span corresponds to a range span. There will be many such range spans out from the radar. The range span is determined by the width of the pulse as it propagates out. For example, a pulse of width τ has a gate length given by:

$$l = c\tau/2 \text{ metres}$$

where c is the velocity of light, and the factor of 2 is because the wave must propagate out and return in the time τ. For $\tau = 1$ μs, $l = 150$ m. Within a practical radar there are thus many bins or gates, each corresponding to this range span. Figure 2.2 shows diagrammatically how the many targets are sorted. After the pulse is transmitted the antenna is connected to the receiver which is in turn connected to the first range gate. There is a close target present which is stored in this gate. As the echo period goes on, the receiver is successively connected to each range gate until at the end of the period it dumps its signal into the last gate. It can be seen that there are five targets at various ranges. After this, the antenna is connected to the transmitter so that the next pulse can be transmitted. Whilst this happens the range gates are emptied into the computer for processing.

Pulse Repetition Frequency (PRF)

The radar does not send out a single pulse to detect a target but will repeat the above sequence many times per second. This repetition helps to confirm the detection made by the first pulse. The speed of repetition is called the pulse repetition frequency (PRF). Figure 2.3 shows the waveform of transmitted and received pulses for two targets, one close and the other at a longer range. The close target echo returns shortly after the pulse has left the radar whilst the distant one returns much later in time. Notice also that the return from the distant target is smaller than that from the closer one due to the spreading out of the radar energy as it propagates and also to wave attenuation in the atmosphere. If the next pulse were sent out before the distant target return arrives, the timing circuits would be confused and an ambiguous measurement might take place. Thus the time between pulses T is arranged to correspond to the outward and return time for targets at the maximum possible range of detection, t_{max}. Returns from beyond this range will be so small that they will not usually be detected. T is given by:

$$T = t_{max} = 2R_{max}/c$$

As $PRF = 1/T$, for a maximum range of, for example, 30 km, the PRF is 5 kHz. This is a typical PRF for a medium range radar. Very long range surveillance radars will have much lower PRFs of the order of a few hundred Hertz, whilst very short range radar may have PRFs greater than 10 kHz.

If a very large target was just beyond the maximum range, its radar echo might just be detectable. However, the radar receiver will be switched off whilst the next pulse is transmitted and the radar will not see this target. Ranges when this occurs are said to be 'blind', as illustrated in Figure 2.4. In addition to distant blind ranges there will, of course, be a blind range close to the radar as near targets will return an echo when the radar is still transmitting. This range is typically no more than a few hundred metres.

It is sometimes necessary to operate a long range radar with a high PRF, particularly when velocity measurement is required using the Doppler effect, for example, in an air intercept radar. In this case, as shown in Figure 2.4, both blind and ambiguous ranges are present. To overcome these problems the PRF can be

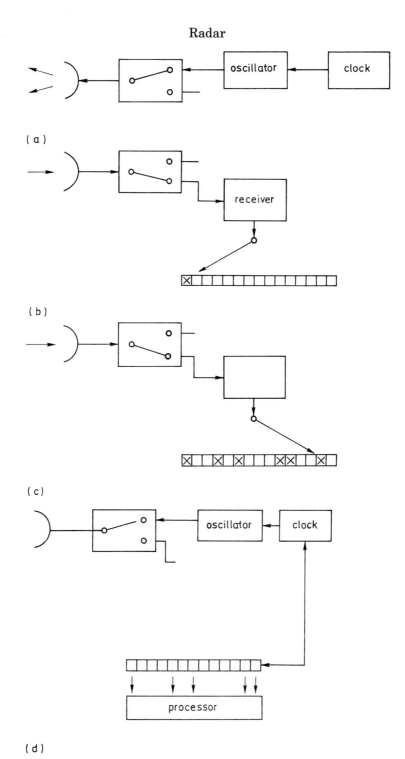

Fig. 2.2   Range gated radar action within one transmit/receive echo period.
(a) Transmit pulse, (b) receive near in echoes, (c) receive far out echoes, (d) finish
range scan and put received signal in computer

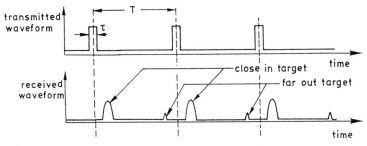

FIG. 2.3   Waveforms in pulse radar

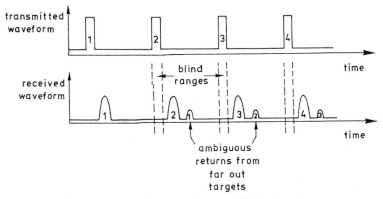

FIG. 2.4   Waveforms in pulse radar showing blind and ambiguous ranges

changed during operation. Radars of this type have what is known as multiple PRF. This technique is becoming widely used in many other military applications as a counter to deception jamming. The PRF, together with the radar frequency and antenna scan rate, are important characteristics that enemy electronic support measures (ESM) receivers will monitor in order to fingerprint a radar and hence determine its likely purpose. Radar electronic warfare (REW) is discussed in more detail in Chapter 9.

Radar Performance Evaluation

The key parameters that allow evaluation of radar performance, comparison between radars and comparison between radars and other surveillance devices, are range capability in varying weather conditions and resolution. The factors that determine these include antenna design, detection methods and frequency of operation. All these aspects are now considered.

Antenna Design

The radar antenna is an important component that features both in the calculation of radar range and resolution. Antenna performance is mainly characterised by its radiation pattern as shown in Figure 2.5. This represents how much power a transmit antenna projects in a given direction; or, if the same antenna is used as a receiver, the receive sensitivity in that direction. Figure 2.5 shows that the antenna has a well defined main beam and many small sidelobes in other directions. The function of the antenna is to project as much of the radar energy in this main beam direction whilst minimising sidelobes.

In practice the antenna may consist of a reflector antenna, an array of small radiators or one of a number of other types occasionally used. Chapter 4 describes in detail the practicalities of antenna technology. Here the important principles of antenna performance specification are given. The degree to which the antenna concentrates power in a given direction gives rise to the idea of power gain or, more simply, gain. It should be stressed that this is not gain in the sense of amplification as the antenna is a passive device and will always radiate less power than its input due to inherent losses. Gain is defined as the increase in power radiated in the main beam compared to that radiated by a non-directive antenna, fed with the same power. The non-directive radiator is called an isotropic antenna and its radiation pattern, plotted in Figure 2.5, is circular. In fact, an isotropic antenna is physically impossible to build but nevertheless forms a useful reference. If gain is given in decibels the unit of gain is dBi, that is dB with respect to isotropic. A decibel is 10 times the logarithm of the quantity considered. In this case if G is the antenna gain with respect to isotropic in numbers the gain in decibels is:

$$G_{db} = 10 \log_{10}(G)$$

Gain for practical radar antennas ranges from a few dBi to 50 to 60 dBi.

High gain is advantageous as it increases the amount of power radiated in a specific direction. High gain also implies large area and this also increases the receive sensitivity in that direction. Both these serve to increase the echo strength and hence enhance the radar range.

Power gain, G, is related to antenna size and operating frequency:

$$G = \frac{4\pi A \eta}{\lambda^2}$$

where A is the physical area of the antenna aperture and η is the antenna efficiency. λ is the operating wavelength. The aperture is an imaginary plane at the front face of the antenna. For an array it is the area occupied by the array elements; for a reflector it is the area defined by the reflector rim. This equation is useful for large antennas but is not accurate for dipoles or whips where the aperture cannot be easily defined.

Antenna efficiency is determined by a number of factors, including resistive loss, aperture distribution tapering and reflector spillover. Resistive loss occurs when the antenna is made of metal that is not perfectly conducting or contains dielectric material that is not lossless. In general, resistive loss is small, contributing to a few per cent reduction in efficiency. However, in some new printed circuit antennas resistive loss may be significant.

Aperture distribution tapering is an antenna design technique that allows the sidelobes to be reduced so that clutter or jamming outside the main beam can be

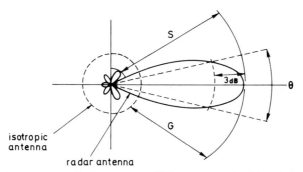

FIG. 2.5   Radar antenna radiation pattern. (G is antenna gain, θ is antenna beamwidth and S is sidelobe level.)

rejected. Figure 2.5 shows how the sidelobe level is defined. In radar antennas it represents the level of the highest sidelobe. The significance of the sidelobe level is discussed later but it can be said here that a highest sidelobe level of -40 dB is considered to be good for a large radar antenna. In general, larger antennas will have lower sidelobes in the region away from the main beam. Figures 2.6a and 2.6b show what tapering of the aperture distribution means. The electric field in the aperture plane of a reflector antenna is plotted, although the concept of tapering applies equally to all other antenna types. If this distribution is uniform, maximum gain occurs with no loss due to tapering. However, sidelobes are relatively high. If the electric field distribution reduces gradually from the aperture centre to the edge, both the sidelobes and the gain reduce. Table 2.1 relates tapering loss to sidelobe level. Typically a loss of 1–2 dB may be expected in a large radar antenna.

Figure 2.6c illustrates what is meant by reflector antenna spillover. A practical reflector feed will illuminate the reflector as required but a small amount of radiation will inevitably miss the reflector. This is spillover loss and will be of the order of a decibel or so. In reflectors, spillover and tapering loss are interrelated and their combined effect is such that small reflectors may have a 60% efficiency whilst good design of large types may increase it to nearer 80%.

To conclude this discussion on antenna gain, Table 2.2 gives an example of an antenna gain calculation.

The final antenna parameter, defined in Figure 2.5, is beamwidth. This is the width of the beam at its half power or -3 dB points. Narrow beamwidth is an important asset in that it results in good resolution and accuracy. The beamwidth θ is given by:

$$\theta = K\lambda/a \text{ radians}$$

where a is the antenna width in the plane in which the beamwidth is defined, for example, the vertical or horizontal planes. The antenna may have different beamwidths in these two directions. λ is the wavelength of operation and K is a factor determined by the aperture distribution, given in Table 2.1. It is apparent that as sidelobe level is reduced, beamwidth increases.

Polarisation of an antenna or electromagnetic wave is another important characteristic. The antenna will radiate or receive electromagnetic waves which are oriented in specific ways. A vertically polarised antenna produces a wave

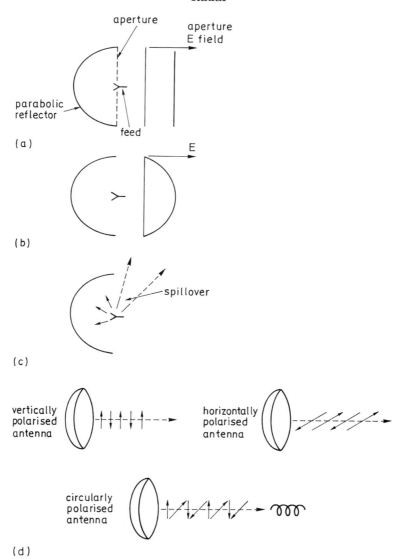

FIG. 2.6 Antenna design. (a) Reflector with uniform aperture field distribution, (b) reflector with tapered aperture field distribution, (c) spillover loss in reflector antenna, (d) antenna polarisation

whose electric component vibrates in the vertical plane, as in Figure 2.6d. This wave will not be received at all by a horizontally polarised antenna and will only partially be received by a diagonally polarised antenna. For maximum reception antennas should be matched to the incoming wave polarisation. In many radars, linear polarisation, that is horizontal or vertical, is used. In some radars for special roles circular polarisation may be used. Here the wave rotates as it propagates away from the antenna, as in Figure 2.6d, and describes a corkscrew motion. As expected, the corkscrew can be left- or right-handed. A left-handed antenna cannot receive right-handed waves and vice-versa. However, a circularly polarised

TABLE 2.1

Sidelobe level, gain loss and beamwidth factor K
due to aperture distribution tapering

Sidelobe level (dB)	Gain loss (dB)	Beamwide factor, K
−13	0.0	0.88
−20	0.8	1.15
−30	1.7	1.45
−40	2.4	1.66

TABLE 2.2

Gain of Circular
Parabolic Reflector at
10 GHz

Aperture diameter	= 1 m
Aperture area, A	= 0.78 m^2
Efficiency, η	= 0.6
Wavelength, λ	= 0.03 m
$G = 4\pi A\eta/\lambda^2$	= 6,580 = 38.2 dBi

antenna will receive any orientation of linearly polarised wave but with 3 dB loss of power. Such antennas are especialy useful in the electronic warfare field.

Some important deductions about antenna design can be drawn from the foregoing:

• For maximum radar range, gain should be high which implies large antennas.
• For best resolution, beamwidth should be small implying large antennas or high frequency operation.

In general a large antenna is contrary to the military requirements for ruggedness, portability and covertness. However, the above performance factors are crucial and many of the longer range radars described later have very large antennas.

Maximum Detection Range and the Radar Equation

The maximum detection range is controlled by several component parts of the radar operation. These can be seen in Figure 2.1 and are identified specifically in Figure 2.7. The first of these components, the radar oscillator, generates a power P_t. The larger the power, the longer the range. If the radar is pulsed and the ratio of pulse period T to pulse width τ (Figure 2.3) is N, then the average power needed to generate the peak power P_t is P_t/N. For example, with $\tau = 1$ μsec and PRF = 5 kHZ ($T = 0.2$ ms), $N = 200$ and only about 5 kW average power is required to generate a 1 MW pulse.

This power is passed to the antenna which will have a directional beam. When radiated by the antenna the power is spread over an increasing area determined by the range and beamwidth as it propagates to the target, as in Figure 2.7c. This spreading decreases the power density of the electromagnetic wave by a factor of r^2, where r is the range. In addition to this spreading loss, the wave is also

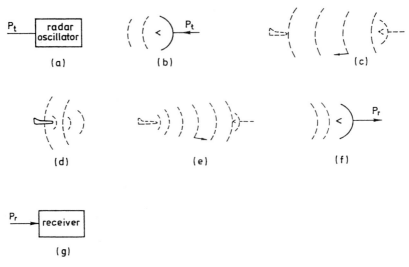

FIG. 2.7   Steps in radar action used to derive range equation

attenuated by scattering and absorption in the atmosphere. This is discussed later in the section on the best operating frequency.

The amount of power reflected from the target as in Figure 2.7d, is determined by its size, shape, aspect and material. Radar wavelength and polarisation are also important. In general, large targets with flat metallic surfaces at right angles to the radar direction will provide the largest returns. Practical targets consist of many reflecting surfaces, some of which predominate, such as the flat side of a tank, the wings of an aircraft and fins on a projectile. The net echo is the resultant of these many reflections. Destructive and constructive interference between these give rise to large variations in the return, as Figure 2.8 shows. The effect also gives rise to variations in the apparent target position, known as 'hot spot wander', 'amplitude fading' and 'glint'. All these target noise effects are important contributions to noise in the radar detection process described later in this section, and also to accuracy considerations.

To gain an idea of the magnitude of the target echo the example of a metal sphere is now considered. A sphere of radius a intercepts power from the incident wave proportional to the projected area of the sphere, that is πa^2. If losses in the metal are neglected, all this power is re-radiated and, because the sphere is symmetrical, it re-radiates isotropically acting as an antenna of power gain $G=1$. The radar cross section (RCS) or radar echoing area (REA) σ of the sphere is simply πa^2. For example, a 1 m diameter sphere has $\sigma = 0.78$ m^2. Most practical targets are not symmetrical and do not re-radiate isotropically. Thus the RCS will not, in general, be equivalent to the silhouette area. Table 2.3 gives values of RCS for typical targets. Reduction of target RCS is now an important technique in the REW field. Some techniques used are to shape the target to reflect the incident energy away from the radar or to apply radar absorbent material (RAM) to the surface.

Upon reflection from the target the radar wave will suffer a further reduction in strength by r^2 due to spreading loss and further atmosphere loss, shown in Figure 2.7e. A power proportional to the antenna effective aperture A_e will be

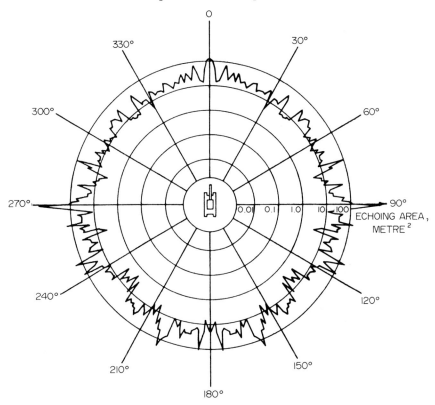

FIG. 2.8 Typical radar cross section (RCS) of tank target

TABLE 2.3

Typical Radar Cross Section (RCS)
Values

Target	RCS (m²)
Ship	>1,000
Large aircraft, plan view	500
Large missile, plan view	100
Large aircraft, slant view	10
Small aircraft, slant view	2–5
Tank	1–10
Missile	0.03
Bomb	0.005
Shell	0.0005

absorbed by the antenna on receive, as in Figure 2.7f. The effective aperture A_e is related to the physical aperture A by the antenna efficiency η so that $A_e = A\eta$. This received power P_r will be transferred directly to the radar receiver, as in Figure 2.7g. All these effects are contained in the radar range equation. This is:

$$P_r = \frac{P_t G \sigma A_e}{16\pi^2 r^4 L}$$

where L includes the atmospheric loss and loss in connecting cables. An alternative form of the radar equation is obtained by replacing the receive aperture size A_e by $G\lambda^2/4\pi$ to give:

$$P_r = \frac{P_t G^2 \lambda^2 \sigma}{64\pi^3 r^4 L}$$

where it is assumed that the same antenna is used for transmit and receive. To estimate the maximum range of the radar the first equation can be rearranged so that:

$$r_{max}^4 = \frac{P_t G \sigma A_e}{16\pi^2 L P_{rmin}}$$

As the received signal will be minimum at maximum range, P_{rmin} must be greater than the minimum detectable signal. Table 2.4 shows calculations based on this equation for short and medium range radars designed to detect a small aircraft. The large increase in peak power coupled with the increased antenna size needed to increase the range significantly is very apparent.

TABLE 2.4

Maximum Range Calculations for Typical Short and Medium Range Radars

Short Range Radar

P_t	$= 100$ W (peak)
G	$= 6,600$ } 1 m diameter circular dish
A_e	$= 0.47$ m² } with 60% efficiency at 10 GHz
σ	$= 2$ m²
L	$= 3$
Min detectable signal	$= 10^{-13}$ W
Max range	$= 10.7$ km

Medium Range Radar

P_t	$= 100$ kW (peak)
G	$= 8,773$ } 2 m diameter circular dish
A_e	$= 2.5$ m² } with 80% efficiency at 5 GHz
σ	$= 2$ m²
L	$= 100$
Min detectable signal	$= 10^{-13}$ W
Max range	$= 40.8$ km

Detection of Radar Signals

When an echo returns from a target the radar receiver has to decide whether it is indeed a target return or just a large noise signal. This process is called radar detection, and as both target return and the noise have random characteristics the process is statistical and involves what is known as probability of detection.

The process consists of comparing the received power with a pre-assigned threshold level. Figure 2.9 illustrates the waveforms involved. These are similar to

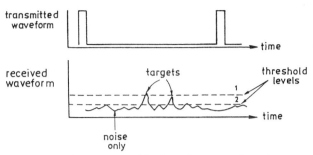

FIG. 2.9   Waveforms involved in the radar target detection process

those of Figure 2.3 but now the receive waveform includes the effect of noise on the received signal. If threshold level 1 is selected, the return from the first target exceeds it and is thus considered to be a target. However, the second target, which gives a smaller return, has been missed. Thus the radar has only a moderate probability of detection. If threshold 2 is chosen, both targets will be seen and the detection probability is increased. However, the noise now also exceeds the threshold at several points. These constitute false alarms and are undesirable. Lowering the threshold has increased the false alarm rate (FAR). Very low false alarm rates are required for critical radars, for example in the detection of intercontinental ballistic missiles. Higher rate can be accepted in other applications, however, and may indeed, for example, serve to reassure the small BSR operator that it is functioning. The threshold level may be controlled by the operator but in many cases will be automatically varied, both throughout the pulse period and between pulses. Radars that vary the threshold to keep FAR constant are termed constant false alarm rate (CFAR) radars.

A critical parameter for good detection probability with low FAR is the signal to noise ratio at the detector. High signal to noise ratio gives good detection probability. A typical value can be obtained by assuming that the external noise is small and that the only noise present is due to random thermal agitation in the receiver. This noise power is given by:

$$N = kTBF$$

where k is Boltzmann's constant and T is the receiver temperature. At ambient conditions $T = 290K$ and $kT = 4 \times 10^{-21}$ W/Hz. B is the receiver bandwidth. For an optimum matched receiver $B = 1/\tau$ where τ is the pulse width. F is the receiver noise factor, which is a measure of how much extra noise the receiver amplifiers add. Assuming that $\tau = 1\ \mu s$ and that $F = 10$, the noise power is $N = 4 \times 10^{-14}$ W. An additional technique in practical radar detectors is to integrate several pulses to improve the detection probability. In practice as many as 30 pulses or more may be integrated. Let us here assume that 14 pulses are integrated in this detection process. Integration is not perfect and this can be characterised by an integration efficiency of about 0.6. Thus the received signal of $P_r = 10^{-13}$ W (Table 2.4) is increased by a factor of (14×0.6). The overall signal to noise ratio is thus given by:

$$\frac{S}{N} = \frac{10^{-13} \times 14 \times 0.6}{4 \times 10^{-14}} = 21$$

Here the signal is well above the noise level and good detection will result. For surveillance radars signal to noise ratios below 10 may be acceptable. For target tracking with maximum accuracy a ratio of the order of 1,000 may be necessary although in many applications lower values may be acceptable. Determination of detection probability and FAR also depends on many other factors and the specific application. Typical probabilities are greater than 90% with a wide range of FARs greater than approximately one every 10 minutes.

Radar Resolution

Resolution is defined as the ability to distinguish between two closely spaced targets. The distance between two resolvable targets must be defined in each of the dimensions of measurement, which are typically for a radar, range, azimuth, elevation and velocity.

Range Resolution

Range resolution is determined by the pulse width. Figure 2.10a shows that if the pulse width is large the returns from the two targets will overlap and hence they will not be resolved. If the pulse were made shorter, as in Figure 2.10b, resolution would take place. The down range distance between targets R_r is given by:

$$R_t = c\tau/2$$

where c is the velocity of light. For $\tau = 1$ μs, for example, $R_r = 150$ m.

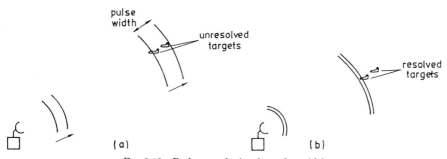

FIG. 2.10   Radar resolution by pulse width

Angular Resolution

The angular resolution in azimuth and elevation is determined by the antenna beamwidth θ and the range r as shown in Figure 2.11. The targets are just resolved when their cross range distance apart R_θ is given by:

$$R_\theta = r\theta$$

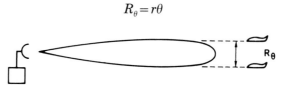

FIG. 2.11   Radar resolution by antenna beamwidth

The antenna beamwidth is given by $\theta = K\lambda/a$ so that:

$$R_\theta = rK\lambda/a$$

where K is the beamwidth factor (Table 2.1), λ is wavelength and a is antenna size. For the 5 GHz medium range radar, analysed in Table 2.4, which had a 2 m antenna diameter, θ is about 1.7°, giving $R_\theta = 1{,}224$ m at 40.8 km range.

Velocity Resolution

Velocity measurement by Doppler processing is described in Chapter 3. In simple terms the target return is frequency shifted by a moving target. If this frequency shift is measured by passing the signal through a series of filters or velocity gates, analogous to the range gates of Figure 2.2, a velocity measurement can be made. The resolution of the velocity measurement is defined as how far apart in speed two targets must be to go into adjacent velocity gates. This is an important method of target discrimination when the targets occupy the same range gate and are not resolved by the antenna beamwidth. The velocity resolution R_v is dependent on the width of the Doppler filters. The Doppler shift f_D is given by $f_D = 2v/\lambda$ where λ is the wavelength and v is the radial target velocity. For a Doppler filter of width f Hz, the target velocity difference for resolution R_v is thus given by:

$$R_v = f\lambda/2$$

For $f = 100$ Hz, $R_v = 3$ m/s at 10 GHz ($\lambda = 0.03$ m).

Radar Accuracy

Radar accuracy is defined as the difference between a target's actual position or velocity and that indicated by the radar. It is critically dependent on resolution. It is clear that narrower pulse widths, beamwidths and velocity gates can give improved accuracy. As radar measurements are subject to noise-like perturbations, accuracy must be specified statistically. Accuracy is best expressed in terms of the standard deviation, σ_R, of the error in each parameter being measured. Sixty-six per cent of all measurements will be within one standard deviation of the correct result. The accuracy is given by:

$$\sigma_R = CR/\sqrt{(S/N)}$$

where C is a constant that depends on the detailed design of the radar. R is the resolution in either range, angle or velocity. It is thus clear that low errors require good resolution and a good signal to noise ratio. These two conditions sometimes conflict and require compromise in design. If the above radar has $C = 1$ and $S/N = 36$, the standard deviation in the range measurement is 25 m and in angle is 204 m.

Choice of Radar Frequency

The best radar frequency for any particular application is dependent on a number of factors including both technical and commercial. However, two dominate: atmospheric attenuation and resolution.

The radar range equation given earlier includes a loss factor, L, to take account of atmospheric loss. It also includes miscellaneous losses in the radar system such as dissipative losses in connecting cables and waveguides and losses due to impedance or polarisation mismatches. In general, radar system losses are kept low by good design and it is atmospheric losses that are most important. Figure 2.12 shows how atmospheric attenuation varies with frequency for clear

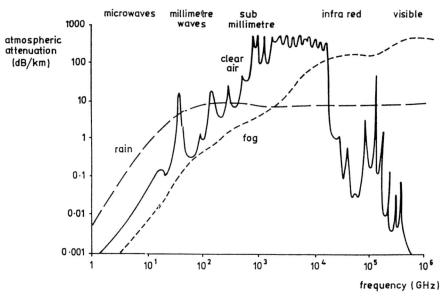

FIG. 2.12   Atmospheric attenuation

air, rain of 25 mm/hr and fog. The attenuation scale is in decibels per kilometre so that L is given by:

$$L = 10^{(2rA/10)}$$

where r is the radar range in kilometres and A is the atmospheric attenuation in decibels per kilometre. For the short range radar example of Table 2.4, A at 10 GHz is 0.08 dB/km. As the range is 10.7 km, then $L = 10^{(2 \times 10.7 \times 0.08/10)} = 1.48$. An additional system loss factor of 2.02 makes up the total loss factor of 3 given in the table. In moderate rain $A = 10$ dB/km, giving $L = 138$. Reworking the calculation of Table 2.4 with $L = 138 \times 2.02 = 279$ gives a maximum range of 3.4 km. From these calculations and Figure 2.12 several important conclusions can be drawn:

• Atmospheric attenuation increases rapidly with frequency.
• Below 10 GHz clear air attenuation is very small.
• Above 10 GHz there are preferred windows for acceptable propagation, in between the attenuation peaks, notably at 36 GHz, 94 GHz and 150 GHz. Range capability reduces significantly at these higher frequencies.
• Rain significantly worsens attenuation and hence range above 10 GHz, but is less important below that frequency.

- Fog and other battlefield obscurrants such as cloud, smoke and dust do not affect radar operation.

Radar angular resolution, R_θ, is dependent on antenna beamwidth which is in turn dependent on frequency. The equations given previously can be rearranged to illustrate this:

$$R_\theta = rc/fa$$

where r is range, c is the velocity of light, f is frequency and a is antenna size. As frequency increases R_θ becomes smaller, giving improved resolution and accuracy.

TABLE 2.5

Radar Characteristics

High frequency —short range
—good resolution
Low frequency —long range
—poor resolution

Table 2.5 summarises the important conclusions. In general, if long range operation is needed, frequencies lower than a few Gigahertz are used. However, resolution will be relatively poor. If good resolution is required, high frequencies must be employed, as in the millimetric wavelength missile seeker heads, explained in Chapter 8, that operate at 94 GHz. In this case range is severely limited to the order of a few kilometres but this is sufficient in this application and these types now form an important radar class. Of course, in between the frequency extremes there are a large number of radars possessing intermediate character-istics and some of these are described in Chapters 5 to 9.

3

Further Radar Techniques

Scope

In Chapter 2 the essentials of pulse radar were explained together with other important ideas such as maximum range and resolution. Modern radars use other techniques to meet the demanding needs of military applications. Primary amongst these is the Doppler technique, which is discussed here alongside the use of circular polarisation, pulse compression, tracking and scanning methods and synthetic aperture radar.

Doppler Radar

The Clutter Problem

The energy radiated from a pulse radar can be considered to form a moving volume, known as the resolution cell, shown in Figure 3.1. The cell length is

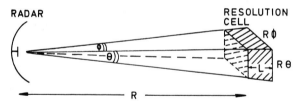

FIG. 3.1   Radar resolution cell (θ is elevation beamwidth, ϕ is azimuth beamwidth and R is range)

equivalent to the range resolution and is therefore determined by the pulse length τ. The cell width and height are equivalent to the angular resolutions and are therefore determined by the antenna beamwidths and range. Good radar design aims to minimise the volume of the cell to maximise the resolution and accuracy. However, its reduction has an additional important benefit. This can be explained by some examples illustrated in Figure 3.2. In Figure 3.2a a ground based radar is looking for ground targets. Here the resolution covers an area on the ground given by the pulse width and the antenna azimuth beamwidth. Any obstacle in the area will give rise to a return signal—an echo. The ground itself, trees, buildings and hills, as well as the wanted target, will reflect energy. These other reflections are unwanted and are known as clutter. In some cases the clutter signal may exceed the noise in the radar. It is then appropriate to calculate signal to clutter levels rather than signal to noise levels, as was done in the previous chapter, to estimate

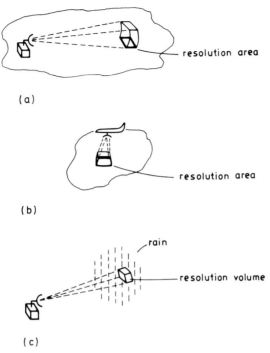

FIG. 3.2   Resolution cell area and volume for clutter calculation

the detection performance. The clutter signal may be found with knowledge of the resolution cell size and the reflectivity of the ground, trees and so on. In Figure 3.2b the clutter area is determined for a downward looking airborne radar by the two antenna beamwidths only. In the case of, for example, an AD radar, rain clutter may be important. Figure 3.2c shows that for volumetric, as opposed to area, clutter the volume of the resolution cell must be known. In these three examples the radar is attempting to detect the target by contrast: that is, by the fact that it reflects more than its surroundings. For a high altitude target viewed by a ground based radar in clear weather this is straightforward. In bad weather the rain may obscure the target. Similarly for ground targets, the ground clutter may be many times greater than the target return. When the clutter problem exists methods such as Doppler processing, circular polarisation and pulse compression must be used.

Some radars, however, are used to image both the surroundings and target. In these cases clutter is not an issue. Here the aim is to deduce target presence by examination of the resulting image. Examples of this are synthetic aperture radar and short range millimetric wavelength imaging radars; they will be described later.

Doppler Radar

When a radar signal is reflected off a moving target the frequency is changed. This is called the Doppler effect and this very important technique allows the target velocity to be estimated but, perhaps more significantly, it means that returns from unwanted stationary objects such as ground, vegetation and clouds can be filtered out. This process of clutter rejection is a powerful one and leads to radar's strong capability to detect moving targets. The very different characteristic Doppler signature of various types of target such as marching men, wheeled or tracked vehicles, helicopters and aircraft also allows target classification to be carried out.

Figure 3.3 shows that an approaching target will increase the radar frequency f_c by the Doppler frequency f_d whilst a target receding at the same velocity will

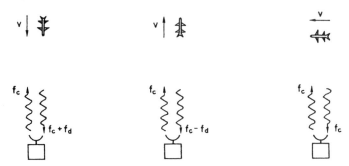

FIG. 3.3   Radar frequencies involved in the Doppler effect

reduce it by the same amount. For a target moving circumferentially around the radar with no radial component of velocity the Doppler frequency is zero. The Doppler frequency is given by:

$$f_d = 2v/\lambda$$

where v is the target velocity radially inwards and λ is the radar wavelength. For a radar with $\lambda = 30$ mm (corresponding to $f_c = 10$ GHz), a vehicle moving towards the radar at 30 mph (13.4 m/s) gives a Doppler frequency of about 900 Hz, a frequency well within the audible range. On the other hand, an aircraft flying at 660 m/s gives a Doppler shift of 44 kHz on the same radar.

To extract the moving target Doppler frequency from the stationary clutter returns, the radar echo must be mixed with a signal at the original radar frequency. Figure 3.4 shows how this is done in a continuous wave, non-pulse radar.The radar transmits at f_c continuously by use of a circulator. The circulator passes radar energy from one connection to that on its right whilst leaving that on its left isolated. This is equivalent to a transmit receive cell in a pulse radar. Thus the energy from the oscillator goes direct to the antenna and not to the receiver where its high power level would burn out the sensitive receiving diode. The radar return, however, is passed from the antenna direct to the receiver. The radar return consists of the incoming target echo at $f_c + f_d$ together with energy reflected from the stationary ground or rain clutter at f_c.

These signals are received and passed to the mixer. The mixer effectively subtracts the frequencies of the two signals. The output thus consists of $(f_c + f_d) - f_c = f_d$ for the target signal and $f_c - f_c = 0$ for the clutter signal. The high pass clutter filter will reject zero frequencies. Thus the clutter is suppressed whilst

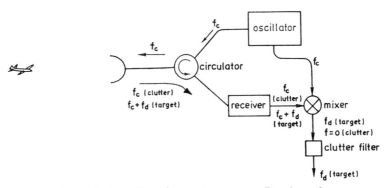

FIG. 3.4   Operation of a continuous wave Doppler radar

the target signal can be measured to establish the speed or to classify the target type. Figure 3.5 shows the transmission characteristic of a typical high pass filter. It is clear that it only passes the higher Doppler frequencies and has a gradual cut off down to zero Doppler. In fact clutter will possess a range of Doppler frequencies due to, for example, wind blown tree movement or the motion of driving rain. The filer must suppress these whilst passing target Doppler. In practical radars it is usual to specify a target minimum speed of a few mph to allow reasonable clutter suppression by such filtering. Doppler blindness and ambiguities also shown in Figure 3.5 are explained later.

Target classification can be achieved by comparing the target Doppler signal with a library of known types or more simply by passing the signal direct to headphones so that a trained operator may do the classification. It is relatively easy to tell the difference between a single man, a group of men, a wheeled vehicle, a tracked vehicle or a hovering helicopter. Chapter 5 describes this aspect in more detail for BSRs. It is the rich content of harmonics in the Doppler spectrum from moving targets that makes such classification possible. Figure 3.6 illustrates this by comparing the spectra from a propeller aircraft and a jet. The Doppler frequency due to airframe motion is clearly seen in both case. However, the Doppler tones due to the propellers and compressor blades are clearly different. It may be possible to automate this classification method but it is very dependent on high computer processing power and memory.

Doppler Processing in Pulse Radars

This technique can readily be incorporated into pulse radars. The pulse radar concept shown in Figures 2.1 and 2.2 can be combined with the continuous wave Doppler radar of Figure 3.4 to give Figure 3.7. The master oscillator which runs continuously drives a pulsed amplifier. Not noted in Figure 2.1 but present in most pulse radars is the receiver gain control. The gain is increased progressively throughout the echo period to offset the wave attenuation during propagation. At the beginning of the period when signal returns are high, the gain is low. At the end, when echoes are weak, the gain is maximum. This ensures that equal sized targets give equal sized signals into the detector. The coherent detector of

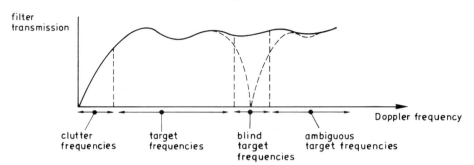

FIG. 3.5   Doppler filter characteristics ——— high pass filter used in continuous wave radar – – – – filtering used in pulse radar

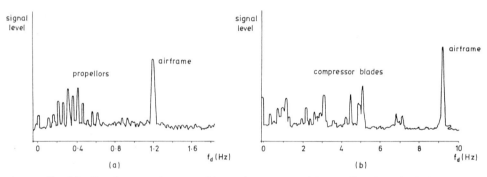

FIG. 3.6   Doppler spectra returned by various targets: (a) propeller aircraft, (b) jet aircraft

Figure 3.7 is identical to the mixer of Figure 3.4. Pulse radars without Doppler processing detect the envelope of the return pulse. They are called non-coherent radars. If Doppler processing with a mixer is used, the system is known as coherent.

Figure 3.8a shows how coherent detection works. The transmit waveform is a series of pulses. The Doppler waveform corresponding to the target motion is impressed on the pulses so that the output of the coherent detector, possibly at intermediate frequency (IF) or baseband, is a series of pulses whose polarity and height vary at the Doppler frequency. If the Doppler waveform itself is required, the pulses may be smoothed with a low pass filter to give the lower waveform of Figure 3.8a.

In low PRF radars for surveillance applications, the Doppler processing method called MTI is used. The echo waveform of Figure 3.8a, the modulated pulse train, is put to the delay line canceller shown in Figure 3.9. The device makes use of the differences between the pulses returning from a moving target. In Figure 3.8a the second return pulse is lower than the first. In the canceller each pulse is divided between two routes. The upper route is through a long line that delays it, so that when it reaches the adder, the following pulse taking the lower route has caught up. In Figure 3.9 the pulses are numbered to make this clear. Pulse 2 has been

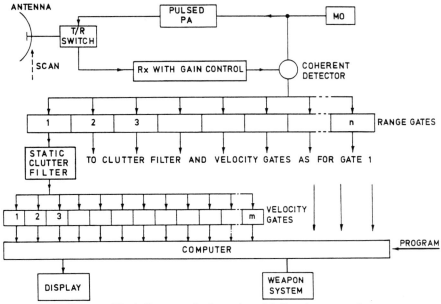

FIG. 3.7   Block diagram of pulse radar with Doppler processing

inverted in the lower path. When pulse 2 and the delayed pulse 1 are added, any differences give a small resultant signal that is amplified and gives an indication on the radar display. If the pulses are returning from a stationary target or clutter, they have equal height as the Doppler frequency is zero. Pulse 2 and delayed pulse 1 exactly cancel. The overall effect is to remove static clutter from the display but allow moving targets to be seen. Figure 3.10 shows a plan position indicator (PPI) display of an area with heavy static clutter. Switching on MTI removes this. The remaining indications on the display are moving targets. Delay line cancellers may operate on three, four or more pulses to give improved rejection of slow moving clutter. Such cancellers are often called transversal filters. The static clutter filter shown in Figure 3.7 may be a delay line canceller or transversal filter. In an MTI radar the output from this filter would be put directly to the computer or display. The operation of a radar using velocity gates is now described.

Radars that use Doppler processing to measure target velocity or to discriminate between moving targets use a slightly different arrangement. Such systems are called pulse Doppler radars and operate with medium or high PRF. How medium and high PRF is defined is described in the next section. Coherent detection shown in Figure 3.7 is used to give the waveforms of Figure 3.8a. The Doppler waveform may be processed by passing it to a bank of narrow bandwidth filters, also called gates. The frequency range of the filter that accepts it gives a measure of the target velocity. Likewise, two targets close in velocity will be resolved if they fall into adjacent velocity gates. Such filtering may also be done digitally using fast fourier transform (FFT) techniques, described in Chapter 4. It is noticed in Figure 3.7 that each range gate may have its own static clutter filter and set of velocity gates. Clearly the system is increasingly complex and expensive. Either the number of

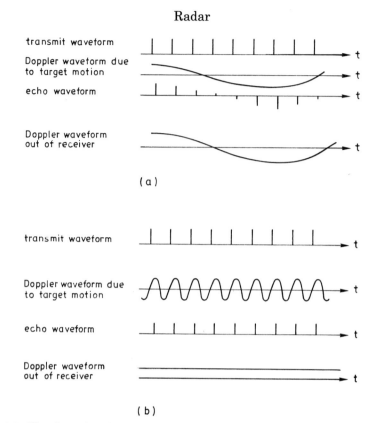

FIG. 3.8   Waveforms in pulse Doppler processing: (a) normal speed target, (b) target at
blind speed

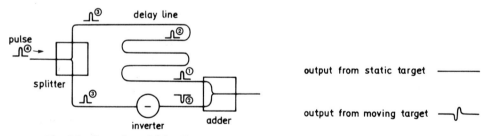

FIG. 3.9   Operation of delay line canceller used in moving target indication (MTI)
processing

gates may be reduced to limit this or very fast digital processing used. Modern
radars very often contain dedicated chips to do this kind of processing.

Blind and Ambiguous Velocity

The way the Doppler signal is extracted from a pulse waveform is shown in
Figure 3.8a. The transmitted waveform is modulated by the target movement so

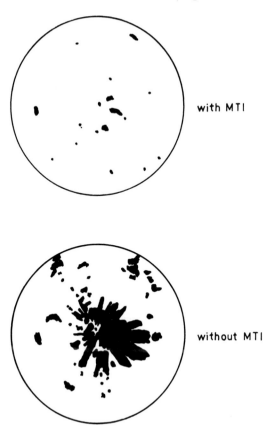

with MTI

without MTI

FIG. 3.10   Plan position indicator (PPI) type radar screen with and without moving
target indication (MTI)

that the pulse heights when smoothed out in the receiver yield the Doppler frequency. It can be seen that many pulses are required to build up the Doppler waveform. If the target is moving at a speed such that the Doppler frequency is equal to the PRF, the situation shown in Figure 3.8b occurs. Here the return pulse modulation is in step with the PRF and no variation of height occurs. When these are smoothed out in the receiver, a waveform with zero Doppler frequency appears. This, of course, will be blocked by the static clutter filter. In effect the whole system now has a filter transmission characteristic indicated by the dotted line in Fgure 3.5. This condition is called a blind velocity, as a target at this speed will disappear from the radar screen. At speeds higher than this the radar is not blind, but ambiguous speed measurements may occur. A very fast target may be mistaken for a slow one. The problem can be avoided by ensuring that the PRF is chosen to be much higher than the maximum likely Doppler frequency of the targets of interest. This can be written as:

$$PRF > 2v_{max}/\lambda$$

where v_{max} is the maximum target speed and λ is the radar wavelength. If the receiver is unable to distinguish between approaching and receding targets, further ambiguity may arise. In this case it is necessary to make the PRF greater than twice the maximum Doppler frequency.

Choice of Pulse Repetition Frequency

PRF can be chosen to avoid blind and ambiguous speed in pulse Doppler radars. However, PRF also affects whether the radar had blind and ambiguous ranges. From the previous chapter this condition is:

$$\text{PRF} < c/2R_{max}$$

where R_{max} is the maximum unambiguous range and c is the velocity of light. To avoid both blind speed and range these two conditions must be combined to give:

$$2v_{max}/\lambda < \text{PRF} < c/2R_{max}$$

In a short range BSR designed to see targets up to a speed of, for example, 30 m/s out to ranges of 6 km, 2 kHz < PRF < 25 kHz. Here a wide range of PRF is possible. However, in the case of a long range radar for detection of very fast targets, there may be no suitable PRF. If, for example, the maximum speed was 300 m/s at a range of 100 km, 20 kHz < PRF < 1.5 kHz and no PRF exists that gives both unambiguous range and speed. This problem can be overcome by repeatedly changing the PRF. This has the effect of moving the blind speeds and ranges, thus exposing targets within them. Similarly, ambiguities can be solved. This may be realised in practice by transmitting a group of pulses, for example 16 or 32 in number at one PRF. Subsequent groups will have a different PRF and so on. This technique is called multiple PRF and is a feature of many modern radars.

The choice of PRF is an important one in radar design. It is similarly important in electronic warfare where it creates a radar 'fingerprint' allowing identification of the radar type by enemy ESM. Table 3.1 gives broad radar classifications according to PRF. In general terms low PRF means less than a few kilohertz and high means greater than about 10 kHz.

TABLE 3.1

Radar Classification by PRF

High PRF	—short range radar for fast targets (blind ranges but not blind speeds)
Medium PRF	—radars for long range surveillance and short range intercept of fast targets, for example aircraft air intercept radars (blind speed and ranges removed by multiple PRF)
Low PRF	—long range surveillance radars (blind speed but no blind range)

Other Important Radar Techniques

Methods of Target Discrimination

The primary method of discriminating between wanted and unwanted targets, or between separate targets, is to have small sized resolution cell, as explained in the last chapter. In this chapter Doppler frequency has been shown to be a fourth dimension in the resolution cell and this aids discrimination.

Notable amongst the other methods of discrimination is examination of target behaviour. A file of target track information over a period of time is created. This information may be range, bearing and elevation in the case of an aircraft target. The characteristics of this track file, such as target speed, rate of turn, maximum altitude, can be compared to known target characteristics. This comparison is known as cross correlation and a set of correlated tracks will be created and displayed with information about target type. Unwanted targets can be discarded. This process also forms the basis of threat evaluation in large surveillance radars and, although it is heavily dependent on computer processing speed and power, it is now a feature of, for example, several of the AD radars described in Chapter 7.

Discrimination can also be improved by using the radar to form an image. In this case the antenna needs to be scanned across the scene, possibly in a raster fashion or simply by linear motion. Scanning is used in airborne ground mapping radars that are designed as navigation aids. In addition to providing a map type display, they can also be used for terrain following, terrain avoidance, moving ground target detection and air-to-ground ranging. Radars operating between 10 to 20 GHz can detect small obstacles such as wires and poles at short ranges. Figure 3.11

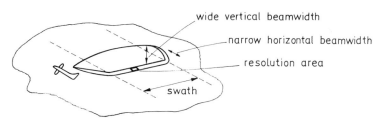

FIG. 3.11   Sideways looking airborne radar (SLAR)

illustrates a slightly different technique that is known as sideways looking airborne radar (SLAR). Here a long antenna is mounted on the aircraft side. The antenna has a very narrow horizontal beamwidth of $0.1°$ or less. Its wide vertical beam is arranged to cover a wide swath, parallel to the aircraft track. Resolution on the ground is determined by the pulse length and horizontal antenna beamwidth and may be, for example, $20\,\text{m} \times 20\,\text{m}$ at 16 km range. The azimuth discrimination worsens with range and this severely limits its use on the battlefield. The synthetic aperture radar technique described later in this chapter has been developed to improve this.

Complex shaped targets, as seen by radar, usually consist of a number of reflecting points distributed over an area and in some cases in depth as well. Recent research has shown that a time record of the position and magnitude of the radar scatter centre as the target moves may give a pattern which is characteristic of the target. Again, such methods are possible only with developing techniques of data storage and processing. This type of information may be enhanced by changing the radar frequency from pulse to pulse (a frequency agile radar) and by periodically changing the polarisation sensitivity of the radar antenna (polarisation agility). The use of such methods for target/clutter separation, and perhaps for non-cooperative IFF are as yet not fully developed, but they appear promising.

Rain Clutter Suppression by Circular Polarisation

The effect of rain clutter is to mask targets by producing stronger returns off the surrounding rain than off the target. Even for radars with a small resolution cell volume rain clutter can be significant. Figure 3.12a shows a target in a rain cloud.

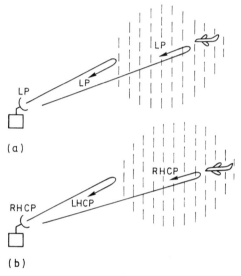

FIG. 3.12   Rain clutter suppression by circular polarisation (CP)

A linearly, that is vertically or horizontally, polarised (LP) radar will see returns in the same polarisation off both target and rain drops. However, if circular polarization (CP) is used, as in Figure 3.12b, the clutter can be much reduced. The radar return from a spherical rain drop has opposite hand of CP. Thus the radar antenna, designed for, say, right hand circular polarisation (RHCP), will not be sensitive to the left hand circular polarisation (LHCP) from the rain. A target with a compex shape, such as an aircraft, will reflect much of the incident energy with the same hand of polarisation. This is because such a target is not circularly symmetrical and has many double bounce reflections, for example, off the fuselage, to the wing and back to the radar. Double bounces change the hand from right to left and back again. The clutter suppression gained using this technique is significant and many radars have a CP option. It should be noted that circularly symmetric targets, such as head-on shells, will also reverse the hand of CP and therefore this technique is much less useful for gun locating radars.

Pulse Compression

Pulse compression is a technique that is now widely used to enhance the range resolution of radars. Figure 3.13 shows how a conventional radar can be adapted. A pulse of length τ_1 is generated as described above. This has a constant radar

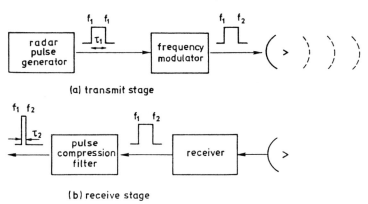

(a) transmit stage

(b) receive stage

FIG. 3.13   Pulse compression

frequency f_1. This pulse is then frequency modulated so that its frequency changes from f_1 to f_2 within the pulse. Alternatively, the generator can be modified to change its frequency during the pulse. This modulated pulse is transmitted and received in the normal way. Separate transmit and receive antennas are shown for clarity, although a single antenna connected to a transmit-receive cell could equally be used. After the receiver it enters the pulse compression filter which is designed to delay signals at f_1 more than those at f_2. This allows the back of the pulse to catch up with the front to produce a narrow pulse with width τ_2. This narrow pulse width determines the range resolution which is consequently much improved. The technique also allows more energy to be put into the pulse on transmit, by making it longer, so that the receive signal to noise ratio, and thus the accuracy, can be improved. Alternatively, for an equivalent resolution and accuracy the transmit power can be reduced. This power reduction technique is an important feature in low probability of intercept (LPI) radars. Pulse compression ratios τ_1/τ_2 of many hundreds can be readily achieved, using compression filters made using surface acoustic wave technology.

Scanning and Tracking Radars

To cover wide angular areas with narrow beams, radars must incorporate some form of scanning. Here the beam is moved across the area of interest by either moving the antenna or by using a fixed phased array. Figures 3.14a and 3.14b illustrate these two types. Alternatively, the antenna may have multiple beams. In this case the antenna has one connector for each beam and the beam positions are fixed relative to the antenna direction. Figure 3.14 shows an antenna with four vertical multiple beams. The technology of phased and multiple beam antennas are discussed further in Chapter 4.

The antenna can scan an area in various ways. It can, for example, scan in a raster fashion, just as the electron beam inside a TV tube scans across the screen. Alternatively, it may adopt a spiral scan starting from the centre and working outwards. In phased arrays a random scan pattern may be used with the beam hopping from point to point as an aid against electronic countermeasures. The

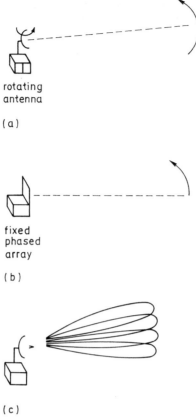

rotating
antenna

(a)

fixed
phased
array

(b)

(c)

FIG. 3.14   Radar scanning: (a) azimuth scanning by rotating antenna, (b) scanning by
fixed phased array, (c) multiple beam antenna

scan ambit is largely dictated by the application. Surveillance radars will cover
the area repeatedly. For example, the *Martello* long range 3D air defence
surveillance radar, described in Chapter 7, combines a 360° azimuth scan by
antenna rotation, with eight multiple beams in the vertical direction. The *MSTAR*
short range battlefield surveillance radar, described in Chapter 5, scans an
azimuth sector by moving the antenna backwards and forwards across the arc. On
the other hand, a tracking radar that is trying to acquire a target will scan an area
where the target is expected and stop as soon as or just after it has found it. It will
then remain on the target direction.

The scanning speed will determine the number of pulses returned from a given
target and the number involved in the detection integration process noted in the
previous chapter. The number N is given by:

$$N = \theta f_{\mathrm{prf}}/6\omega_s$$

where f_{prf} is the PRF, θ is the beamwidth and ω_s is the angular scan rate in rpm.
Assume that the rotation rate of a long range surveillance radar is 10 rpm.
Assuming a beamwidth of 1.7° and 500 Hz PRF, then $N = 14$. It is also evident that
an antenna rotating at this speed will look in the target direction once every 6 s.

This relatively slow data rate is acceptable for long range surveillance, where the situation is fairly slow moving. However, for other applications a faster data rate may be necessary. For instance, an alerting radar for a very short range air defence gun or missile system would typically require an antenna rotation rate faster than one revolution per second. In this case the number of pulses integrated from a single target may be reduced. The trade-off between data rate and detection probability needs careful study in all radar design.

Tracking radars are important and incorporate a range of techniques. As mentioned earlier, once the target direction has been established, at one instant in time, information about subsequent target movement must be obtained to allow the antenna scanning drive to steer it to follow the target. One technique developed early in the history of radar is called conical scan, as in Figure 3.15a. In

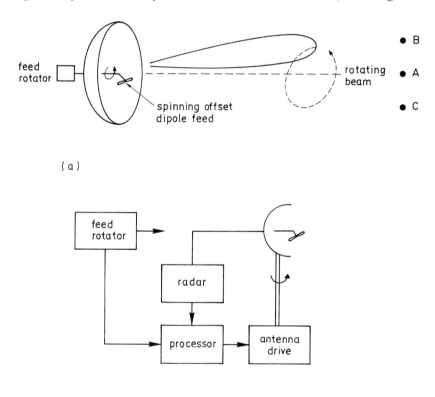

FIG. 3.15   Conical scan tracking: (a) antenna action, (b) tracking loop

this system a parabolic reflector is fed by a dipole offset from the reflector focal point. It produces a beam offset from the reflector boresight. The dipole is rotated around the focal point, producing a beam that rotates around the direction in which the antenna is pointing in a conical pattern. If the target is along the antenna axis at position A, the output from the radar does not vary with time. If it now moves to position B, the radar gives a greater output when the beam scans through this point than when at point C. By synchronising the radar output with the feed dipole position, not only can the presence of a boresight pointing error be detected, but also its direction deduced. In practice this signal is used to generate an error voltage that drives the antenna to the target direction. Tracking in one dimension only is shown for clarity. In reality, tracking in both azimuth and elevation may be needed.

Conical scan tracking is susceptible to target induced noise such as amplitude fading and glint. During the rotation period the signal returning from the target may change and this will induce errors in the tracking signal. An improved system called monopulse reduces this problem. As shown in Figure 3.16a, the antenna has

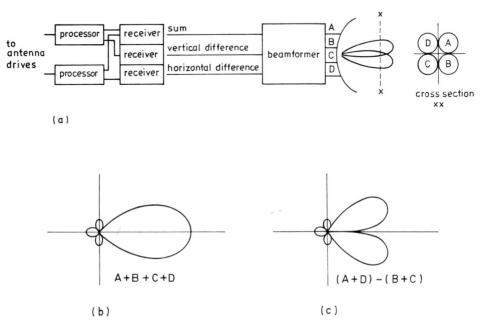

FIG. 3.16   Monopulse tracking: (a) antenna and processing, (b) sum pattern, (c) vertical difference pattern

four multiple beams. The four antenna signals are combined in the beamformer to give a signal corresponding to the sum, that is $A+B+C+D$, a vertical difference beam, that is $(A+D)-(B+C)$ and a horizontal difference beam, that is $(A+B)-(C+D)$. The sum beam and vertical difference beam pattern are shown in Figures 3.16b and 3.16c. When the sum and difference patterns are compared in the processor shown in Figure 3.16a, both the amount of target movement off the antenna boresight and its sense, that is up or down, can be found. This is simultaneously sensed in the horizontal plane and the results used to drive the antenna onto the target direction. The advantage over conical scan of this important method is that it measures target direction within one pulse. This gives it its name monopulse tracking and means that it is much less susceptible to target noise.

The monopulse system shown in Figure 3.16, using four inclined beams, is known as amplitude comparison monopulse. A similar system known as phase comparison is now also used. Four beams, all looking along the antenna axis, are created by the four quadrants of the antenna or indeed by four separate antennas in a close cluster. Target direction is obtained by measuring the relative phase and hence the time of arrival of the target signal at the four antennas. Phase comparison is widely used in arrays, both fixed beam and phased. In this case the array is split into four sections to produce the four beams.

Monopulse systems give target direction with an accuracy of typically 0.01 beamwidths, assuming that only one target is in the antenna field of view. If several targets are present they will give the centroid of the target group to the same accuracy. The technique will not improve radar resolution as this is still determined by the antenna beamwidth, as described in the last chapter.

Synthetic Aperture Radar

The sideways looking airborne radar described earlier has limited resolution, particularly at long ranges, due to its limited antenna size. So it has been developed, by the addition of signal processing, into what is called synthetic aperture radar (SAR). This is capable of very high resolution at very long ranges. The basic action is illustrated in Figure 3.17 where the aircraft with its sideways

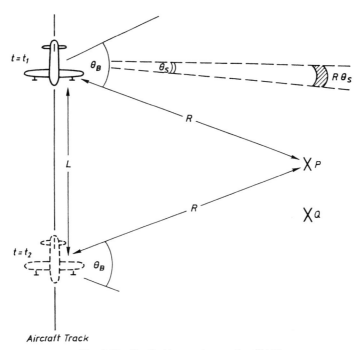

FIG. 3.17 Synthetic aperture radar (SAR)

looking radar flies a distance L. At the start of this path at time $t = t_1$, the object P is just in the edge of the radar antenna beam, which has width θ_B. At the end of the path, at time $t = t_2$, the object is just leaving the other side of the beam. During the time $t_2 - t_1$, the returns from the range corresponding to the target P are processed so that a resolution of $R\theta_s$ is achieved, which corresponds to an apparent beamwidth θ_s. This beamwidth is very narrow and is equivalent to that available if the antenna actually had an aperture size of L. In fact the antenna aperture is much smaller and this gives rise to the term SAR.

The processing technique makes use of the fact that at time $t=t_1$ the target return has a small positive Doppler shift, whereas at a time midway between t_1 and t_2 it has no Doppler shift and at $t=t_2$ has a small negative shift. This Doppler shift is shown in Figure 3.18a. For a second target Q, at the same range but further down the aircraft track, Figure 3.17, the Doppler time characteristic is shown dotted. If

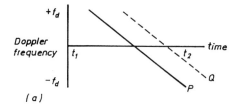

(a)

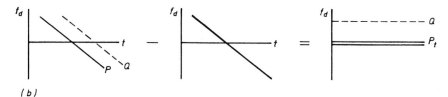

(b)

FIG. 3.18   SAR processing

both these Doppler characteristics, which occur simultaneously, are subtracted from a characteristic generated inside the radar, corresponding to that expected from P, then the characteristic shown in Figure 3.18b results. The returns from P and Q are constant in time but have different frequencies. If this combined signal is now passed through a narrow bandwidth filter centred around $f_d=0$, only the target P will be seen, whilst objects around it will be rejected. Hence a high resolution at point P can be obtained. Range gating is combined with this method so that a horizontal row of picture points is created, as shown in Figure 3.19. The process is now repeated for the radar information gathered during the slightly later period $(t_2+\Delta t)-(t_1+\Delta t)$ where Δt is the small time advance. This will give a return from the area directly next to P, that is incorporating point Q. Thus a high resolution picture is built up pixel by pixel. SAR gives high resolution across the radar look direction, that is parallel to the aircraft flight path, whilst resolution down range from the radar can be obtained by use of narrow pulses. The processing has been simplified here for clarity. In modern SAR the processing may be done digitally.

The resolution obtained by SAR is dependent mainly on the length of the synthetic aperture L. This in turn depends on the actual aperture size of the radar

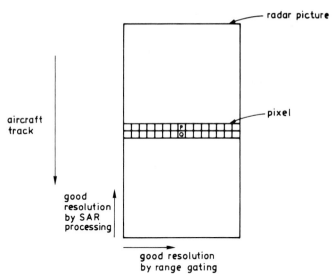

FIG. 3.19   Creation of SAR image

antenna L_a and the radar range, R. L_a determines the beamwidth θ_B and hence the observation time of a single target area. In fact the ground resolution, d_a, parallel to the aircraft track is given by:

$$d_a = L_a/2$$

Thus for an antenna having $L_a = 1$ m, $d_a = 0.5$ m. To approach such resolution in practice requires a very steady aircraft track and very stable radar oscillators.

In general, equal resolution in both directions, parallel to and perpendicular to the aircraft track, is sought. An important problem that affects the use of such airborne imaging radar is the significant shadowing by undulating terrain that low angle sensors experience. In addition the problem of interpretation and dissemination of the radar pictures is not to be underestimated. Flexible operation may to some extent reduce the shadowing problem and the use of combined SAR and MTI techniques may allow faster utilisation of the information. However, this is a developing area and no definite answers can be given yet.

4

Radar Technology

Making Use of the Principles

The principles of radar operation and the fundamental techniques involved have been described in the preceding chapters. Radar technology describes how these principles are implemented in practice. Such implementation is, of course, not easy and was in the past the key to early radar development and is now the key to ever increasing capability. The advent of the cavity magnetron in 1940 and the recent development of phased arrays and high speed digital processing are just some examples of the types of technology that have a profound effect on radar and its use. In this chapter these and other radar technologies are described.

Radar Transmitters and Receivers

Introduction

The previous chapters have indicated that, unlike radio communications equipment, radar usually needs very high levels of transmitted power. This power may be generated by a single device or by a number of low power oscillators and combined in some way. This leads to the distinction between single point or distributed generation which is illustrated in Figure 4.1. Single point generation is simple to engineer and all early radars used this concept. However, it means that the large power has to be generated by a single device. Such a device is generally a microwave vacuum tube, such as a magnetron or a klystron. Vacuum tubes require high voltage supplies which employ heavy transformers. The science of microwave tubes is vast and only some important examples are given below. With the advent of array antennas it was realised that each array element could be driven by its own oscillator. Each oscillator would need to generate only a few watts of power, as the array may contain many thousand oscillators. Also the failure of a few oscillators is unlikely to affect the overall performance very much, giving it a 'graceful degradation' characteristic unlike the possible catastrophic failure of a single point generation system. Semi-conductor oscillators using transistors, Gunn or IMPATT diodes can be used in distributed power generation systems: these require only low voltage supplies. A further advantage is that the oscillator can be integrated into the same circuit as the receiver to form a complete transmit and receive module. However the modules need to be controlled centrally, as indicated in Figure 4.1b, and the module cost is relatively high, leading to very high overall costs. The concept is discussed further in the phased array section of

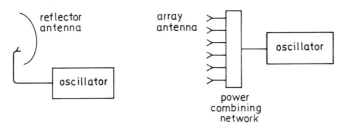

(a)   Single Point Microwave Power Generation

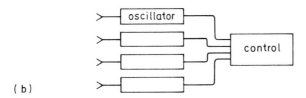

(b)

FIG. 4.1   Radar transmitters: (a) single point microwave power generation, (b)
distributed power generation in radar arrays

this chapter. In this section on radar transmitters, tube technology and some
important solid state oscillators are described.

This contrast in the capabilities of microwave tubes and solid state devices is
further illustrated in Figure 4.2 which shows the likely power levels and operating
frequencies of some of the oscillators mentioned below.

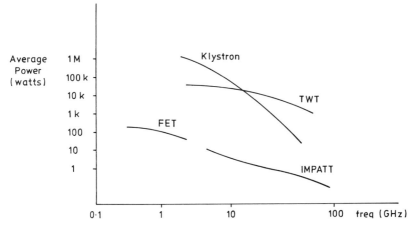

FIG. 4.2   Power levels of common microwave oscillators

The Magnetron

The principle of operation of a cavity magnetron was described in Chapter 1
with Figure 1.7 showing the main components. The frequency is controlled by the
cavity size. The oscillation is maintained by the transfer of energy from the direct

current bias applied across the anode cathode gap to the oscillating magnetic field. This energy is transferred through the electrons given off by the hot cathode. The principle of energy transfer from the dc supply to the electromagnetic field, oscillating at the radar frequency through an electron beam, is common to all microwave valves. As the magnetron is a pulsed oscillator, it cannot easily be used in a coherent radar in which the return pulse must be compared with that transmitted. To enable the magnetron to be used with MTI, it is necessary to make the magnetron phase lock another independent oscillator called a COHO (coherent oscillator). Typical magnetron peak powers are of the order of hundreds of kilowatts (10^3 W) with pulse widths of a few microseconds (10^{-6} s). The efficiency of conversion of dc to microwave power, which is of the order of 50%, is relatively high for vacuum tube device.

The Klystron

In the cavity klystron the electron beam moves in a straight line between the cathode and anode, as shown in Figure 4.3. The fields in the input cavity distort or

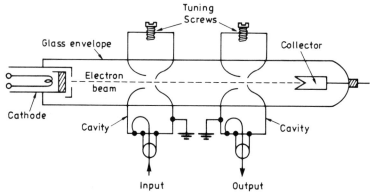

FIG. 4.3   Klystron microwave oscillator

modulate the electron beam passing through it. As the beam moves on, these distortions are naturally amplified within the beam. The electrons then give up some of their power to the output cavity with a resultant overall increase in the microwave signal. In this way the tube is acting as an amplifier. By suitable feedback, between the output and input cavities, an oscillating device can be formed. The importance of the klystron lies in its inherent coherence, making it suitable for a wide range of uses in Doppler radars, both as transmitting valves, amplifiers and also as receiver local oscillators. High powers can be obtained although its bandwidth is narrow, of the order of a few per cent. Continuing development is now resulting in klystrons with higher power and wider bandwidth.

The Travelling Wave Tube

A more continuous interaction between the electron beam and the microwave fields than in the klystron occurs in the travelling wave tube (TWT) shown in

Figure 4.4. Here the fields travel down a helix whose pitch is such that the field and electron beam speed is comparable and efficient exchange of energy can take place. The main advantage of TWT over the klystron is its very wide bandwidth. This comes about as the helix is a non-resonant device, unlike the cavities in the klystron. TWTs will operate over octave bandwidths and would thus be suitable for many electronic warfare uses, such as the generation of jamming.

New Vacuum Tube Developments

In addition to improving the power output, bandwidth and other parameters of microwave tubes, the generation of high power at millimetric frequencies is currently under scrutiny. Likely devices are the millimetre wave TWT, the extended interaction oscillator (EIO) and the millimetre wave gyrotron. Typical pulsed power outputs from an EIO is of the order of hundreds of watts at 100 GHz and proportionately less at higher frequencies.

Solid State Transmitters

Early transistors could operate up to frequencies of a few tens of megahertz. Today diffused bipolar transistors and field effect transistors (FET) using Gallium Arsenide semi-conductor material can operate up to frequencies of tens of gigahertz, making them useful as microwave power generators. Peak power outputs for a bipolar transistor amplifier of up to one kilowatt have been obtained with bandwdths of 10–20%. Efficiencies of 20–40% are not untypical, so in a phased array cooling is a problem. Many heat pipes connected to a heat dissipator are needed.

Higher pulse powers and frequencies can be obtained from oscillator diodes, such as the impact avalanche transit time (IMPATT) device or Gunn diode. Figure 4.5 illustrates the operation of this type of device by the example of a Gunn diode. The diode itself consists of a piece of Gallium Arsenide (GaAs) material. This is biased by placing a dc voltage across it, as shown, and connecting it to a resonant circuit. The resonator could be a waveguide cavity or a microwave circuit, such as microstrip or stripline, as described in the next section. Near to one of the contacts normal random action within the GaAs creates a small imbalance in the number of electrons. With the right conditions this imbalance grows to form a large group of electrons, called a domain, which then drifts across the material to the other contact. When it reaches the contact it creates a burst of current in the resonant circuit. Immediately this happens a new domain forms and drifts across the device. Thus a series of current bursts is created. The time between bursts is governed by the speed of the domain and the length of GaAs block. If this is properly engineered, bursts at the required radar frequency can be generated. For example, operation at 10 GHz requires the domain to move across the device in $1/10^{10}$ s (or 10^{-10} s). The GaAs block itself may be a few micrometres (10^{-6} m) across. The circuit of Figure 4.5 will thus create a continuous wave at 10 GHz. When used in a pulse radar the device would be switched on and off at the required PRF. Such diodes are called transit time devices as the operation frequency depends on the domain transit time. IMPATT diodes work on similar principles. Although such

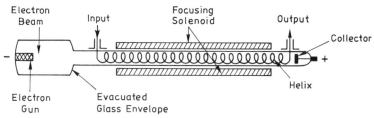

FIG. 4.4   Travelling wave tube (TWT)

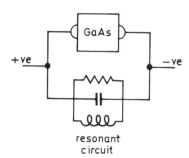

FIG. 4.5   Gunn diode microwave oscillator

oscillators in general provide only a few watts of power, Figure 4.2 shows that operation up to 100 GHz and beyond is possible.

Radar Receivers

The object of the radar receiver is to amplify and detect the presence of the small target echoes in the presence of noise. As noise is present across a wide frequency range the primary method of noise suppression is by filtering. The receiver is sensitive only to signals at or close to the radar frequency. Filtering is easier to achieve at relatively low frequencies, so the reduction of the frequency of the radar signal is an important part of the receiver action. Figure 4.6 shows a block diagram of a radar receiver. The return target echoes together with noise are picked up by the radar antenna. Some amplification, perhaps about 10 to 100 times, takes place at the radar frequency, f_r. This signal is applied to a mixer that combines it with the signal from a local oscillator. The local oscillator is usually tuned slightly higher than the wanted radar frequency, f_{lo}. This gives rise to the term superheterodyne, which means mixing with something higher. The action of the mixer is to form a third signal whose frequency, called the intermediate frequency, f_{if}, is the difference between the other two. Thus:

$$f_{if}=f_{lo}-f_r$$

The intermediate frequency is considerably lower than the radar frequency and is chosen so that useful filtering can take place. For example, if $f_r=10$ GHz, $f_{lo}=10.1$ GHz giving, $f_{if}=0.1$ GHz or 100 MHz. If this is still too high a second

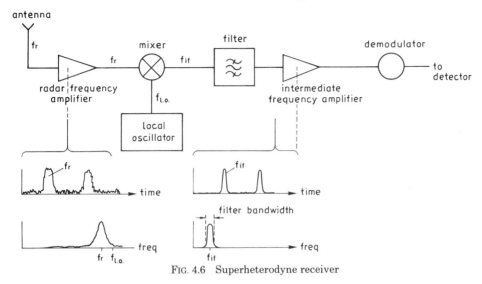

FIG. 4.6   Superheterodyne receiver

mixing stage may take place. After this filtering, high amplification takes place. Typically a 40 dB or more increase in signal may be required to lift it to the few volts necessary for operation of the detector. The filter bandwidth is related to the radar waveform bandwidth. In a so-called matched receiver the bandwidth $B = 1/\tau$, where τ is the pulse length. Thus for $\tau = 1\ \mu s$, $B = 1$ MHz.

The time and frequency waveforms of a signal going through the receiver are also shown in Figure 4.6. On the left hand side pulses from two targets down range have been received. Their frequency spectrum is centred on f_r and the signals are contaminated by noise. On the right the signal frequency has been reduced to f_{if} and some of the noise removed by filtering. In the demodulator the envelope of the pulses at f_{if} is extracted to pass on to the detector where the decision process about whether it is a target or a false alarm is made. This describes non-coherent detection. If Doppler processing is to be done, the phase of the pulse in addition to its envelope is needed and coherent demodulators are used.

Radar Components

Transmission Lines

Figures 4.1 and 4.6 have shown various radar systems as blocks connected by lines. Unlike low frequency circuits, such as hifi amplifiers or power supplies, it is not possible to link radar systems with simple wire interconnections. There are two important reasons why more complicated connecting lines are needed. First, as the wavelength of the radar signal is comparable to the size of the components, the characteristic impedance of the lines becomes important. Figure 4.7 illustrates this point. For full power transmission the generator, line and load impedance must be equal or matched. Typically in many systems 50 Ω is chosen as a common impedance. A second important factor is the loss in the line and the fact that open lines radiate energy, thus increasing the line loss and coupling into other

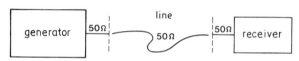

FIG. 4.7   Component characteristic impedance

components. A range of microwave transmission media has been developed, some of which are shown in Figure 4.8. Perhaps the best known is waveguide, as in Figure 4.8a. Here the energy can be launched into the rectangular metal tube over a wide range of frequencies. The wide dimension is about half a wavelength so it is obvious that at low radar frequencies, say 1 GHz, very large waveguides are needed of the order of 200 mm × 100 mm and these are bulky and expensive. Similarly at very high frequencies, say 100 GHz, the waveguide is very small, about 2 mm × 1 mm, and these are hard to make and hence expensive. However, loss and leakage is low. In some cases the loss can be further reduced by silver or gold coating the inside. For high power applications such as feeds to antennas, the waveguide may be pressurised to reduce the risk of voltage breakdown.

A more convenient transmission medium is coaxial line, as in Figure 4.8b. The line consists of two distinct conductors and this means that a very much wider range of frequencies can be carried. The inner conductor is usually supported by dielectric spacers or a solid dielectric core. Microstrip and triplate stripline are related to coaxial line. They can be thought of as coaxial with the inner conductor flattened out and, in the case of microstrip, with the outer unrolled into a single sheet. In both cases the strip conductor is supported by dielectric sheets. The main attraction of these transmission media is that the strip can be formed by the photolithographic etching process, the method by which printed circuit boards are made. They are thus potentially cheap to make.

Coaxial line is widely used to connect component boxes when high power handling is not needed. Microstrip is used widely within receiver and transmitter boxes, as indicated below. Triplate is used for antenna feed networks as well as other purposes. Waveguide, however, remains necessary where very low loss or very high power handling is needed.

Circuit Components

The transmission lines described above form the basis of many circuit components. In all of them, bends, junctions and other shapes can be made to allow circuit operations at the radar frequency to be performed. Two examples are given here to illustrate this idea.

Figure 4.9 shows a filter made in waveguide. A series of screws is let into the waveguide wall. Each screw produces a mismatch in the waveguide. The complete set of screws will give an overall device that is mismatched at most frequencies. At one specific frequency, determined by the relationship between the screw spacing and the wavelength, the filter looks matched, due to the cancelling effect of the individual mismatches. A mismatched device will not transmit the signal from one end to the other. In this way the filter passes a given frequency and rejects all others.

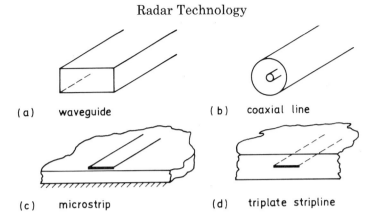

(a)   waveguide   (b)   coaxial line

(c)   microstrip   (d)   triplate stripline

FIG. 4.8   Common microwave transmission lines: (a) waveguide, (b) coaxial line,
(c) microstrip, (d) triplate stripline

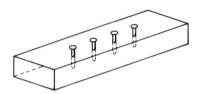

FIG. 4.9   Waveguide filter

Figure 4.10 shows a phase shifter made in microstrip. The circuit shown is etched on the top surface. The dielectric is alumina, a ceramic material. The lower surface is fully metallised. At the line junctions very small diode switches are attached that can be switched on or off by dc control voltages. If the switches are arranged to be in state 1 the phase is related to a direct line length from input to output. When switched to state 2 the effective line length increases and hence the phase of the signal at the output is altered. How this device is incorporated into a phased array is described in the next section.

It is possible to put other components on to the same microstrip substrate, such as mixer diodes, transistors and filters. Thus all the components of the receiver of Figure 4.6 that operate at the radar frequency can be made in one operation. This concept is known as the microwave integrated circuit (MIC). Figure 4.11 shows a microwave system built in this way. Sections of the system, each containing many microwave components, are made on one microstrip circuit and mounted inside a box. Typically each circuit is a few centimetres square. Ultimately all the components could be mounted on a single substrate to simplify manufacture. Connections to the outside world are made through coaxial and other cables.

Microwave devices such as transistors, Gunn diode oscillators and switches are usually made using silicon or GaAs semi-conductor material. They are typically less than one millimetre in size. Many such components can be integrated on to one piece of semi-conductor material to form, for instance, a complete phase shifter with many phase states. This will then be only slightly larger than a single device.

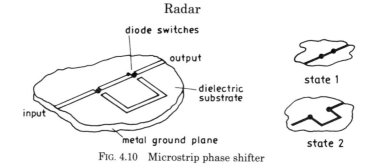

FIG. 4.10   Microstrip phase shifter

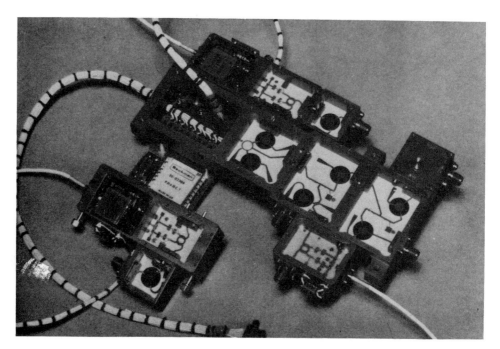

FIG. 4.11   Microwave integrated circuit (MIC) *(Courtesy of CIT)*

These integrated circuits can then be mounted on the ceramic microstrip circuit as above. This is a so-called hybrid circuit as it contains two forms of integration method. Figure 4.12 shows a hybrid circuit. If the complete circuit is made on a single piece of semi-conductor, a monolithic integrated circuit (MMIC) is formed. MMICs are currently being designed for radars, where it is hoped that low costs will be achieved.

Antennas

Antenna technology has advanced significantly in the last two decades with the emergence of both advanced reflector design and, more importantly, phased arrays.

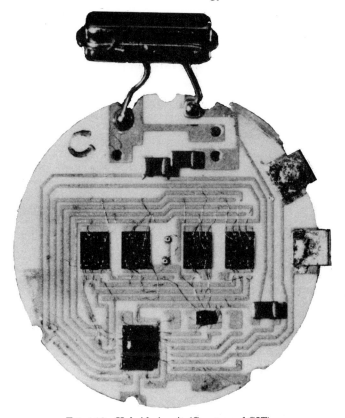

FIG. 4.12   Hybrid circuit *(Courtesy of CIT)*

Reflector Antennas

Compared to a phased array, a reflector antenna is easy to make and is therefore less expensive. It is the preferred antenna for many current radars as witnessed by examples in the second part of this book. The key principle is shown in Figure 4.13

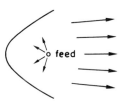

FIG. 4.13   Parabolic reflector antenna

and is the same as that used in vehicle headlights. A parabolic shaped reflector converts the diverging beam from the feed into rays that are nearly parallel. The degree to which the rays are not parallel is the beamwidth of the antenna, as discussed in Chapter 3.

Variously shaped reflectors have been made. If it is remembered that the beamwidth concept can be applied to both the horizontal and vertical directions, then if different beamwidths vertically and horizontally are needed, reflectors with varying aspect ratios will result. Figure 4.14 shows reflectors for (a) a narrow azimuth and wide elevation beam and (b) a wide azimuth and narrow elevation beam. These shapes have in the past been used for surveillance and height finding for AD radars.

FIG. 4.14 Reflector antenna shapes: (a) narrow azimuth, wide elevation beam, (b) wide azimuth narrow elevation beam

In the reflectors seen so far, the feed is directly in front of the reflector. This means that some power coming off the reflector is blocked and long cables from the transmitter/receiver and the feed are needed. An arrangement to overcome these problems is the offset reflector shown in Figure 4.15a. Here only the top half of the

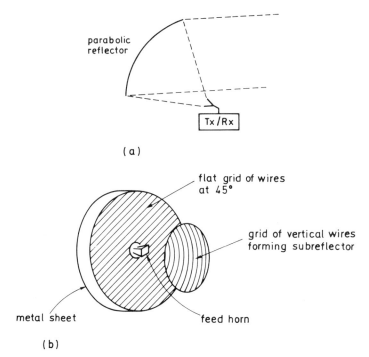

FIG. 4.15 Reflector antennas: (a) offset reflector, (b) twist Cassegrain reflector

parabolic reflector is used so that rays coming off the reflector do not hit the feed, which is mounted directly onto the electronics, so reducing cable loss. Offset reflectors are now widely used in radar systems, an example being the Rapier DN181 *Blindfire* tracking radar described in Chapter 7.

Figure 4.15b shows an important reflector antenna, known as the twist Cassegrain. A Cassegrain antenna is one in which the feed points through a hole in the centre of the main reflector toward a sub-reflector which directs energy back onto the main reflector and hence out into a conventional beam. The advantage of having the feed positioned there is that it eliminates the loss in feeder cables or waveguide necessary for front fed types. In a Cassegrain reflector the transmitter and receiver can be located behind the main reflector and coupled directly on to the feed horn. However, the problem with this configuration is that the sub-reflector may well produce more blockage to the main beam than with front feeding. The answer is to use the polarisation twist technique. In Figure 4.15b the feed radiates vertical polarisation that bounces off the sub-reflector, which is made up of a grid of vertical wires. The main reflector consists of a grid of diagonal wires spaced a quarter of a wavelength in front of a metal sheet. This has the effect of twisting the polarisation coming off the sub-reflector from vertical to horizontal. The sub-reflector is effectively transparent to horizontal polarisation and the energy bouncing off the main reflector thus goes straight through. In addition to removing blockage, the twist Cassegrain reflector allows very simple beam scanning: the feed and the sub-reflector are fixed and the flat main reflector is tilted to move the beam direction. This arrangement has been widely used in missile homing heads and an example for use at 95 GHz is shown in Figure 8.7.

Phased Arrays

If many small antennas are placed side by side an array is formed, with all the properties of directional beams so far described. If the power combining network in Figure 4.1a is fixed and designed so that all the transmit energy is radiated simultaneously, a beam is radiated directly away from the array. This idea is further illustrated in Figure 4.16 by considering what happens on receive. The incident pulse from direction *B* is absorbed by all the elements and travels to the receiver via the interconnecting lines and adding circuit. The lines have equal length so that all the signals reach the receiver in step and add to form a strong pulse. However, if the pulse is now coming in from the side of the antenna in direction *A*, the pulses will not reach the receiver at the same time and hence will not add into a strong signal. This variation in received strength is, in fact, another way of describing the antenna radiation pattern. Fixed beam arrays are used in many radars and when scanning is required will be physically rotated.

If the array interconnecting lines have phase shifters in them, as in Figure 4.17, the way in which the pulses build up can be controlled. For a given arrangement of phase shifters, the time delays introduced can mean that a pulse from direction A can give a strong signal. In effect the radiation pattern peak has been moved to direction *A*. This is the basic principle of a phased array that enables a fixed antenna to scan a narrow beam over a wide sector of interest. The phase shifters may also be associated with variable attenuators. These will be controlled by the

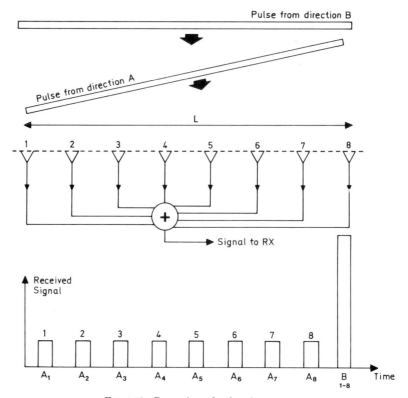

FIG. 4.16   Reception of pulses in an array

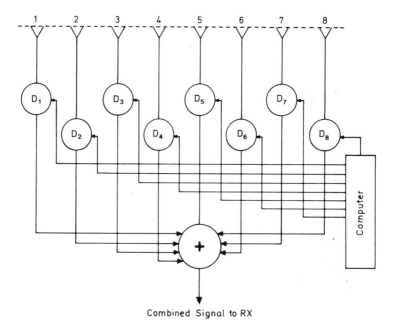

Combined Signal to RX

FIG. 4.17   Phased array operation

computer and will allow aperture tapering, as described in Chapter 2, to be performed to reduce the sidelobes. The typical scan range is up to 45° away from broadside. The phase shifters are switched by computer and may move the beam in a millisecond (10^{-3} s) or less. The very rapid beam control is one of the big attractions of phased arrays and allows, for example, surveillance of large areas to be combined with tracking of many targets. Examples of practical phased arrays are given in Chapters 6 and 7.

Frequency Scanned Arrays

A simple way of scanning the beam from an array, which does not involve phase shifters and a control computer, is shown in Figure 4.18. Each element is connected to a continuous transmission line. As the frequency is changed the

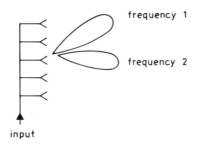

FIG. 4.18   Frequency scanned antenna array

wavelength changes and the effective phase shift introduced by the transmission line changes also. This changes the phase at each element, thus effectively moving the beam by the same principle as described above. If the frequency within the radiated pulse is changed, as described in Chapter 2, the beam will scan within the pulse. The simple hardware needed to implement this is attractive and hence many 3D surveillance radars such as the IUKADGE radar T43 use frequency scanning in elevation combined with mechanical rotation in azimuth.

Foster Scanner

An important method for achieving rapid scanning in one plane is the Foster scanner shown in Figure 4.19. The scanner is used to feed a parabolic cylinder reflector and results in a beam that scans backwards and forwards in a horizontal plane. This is suitable for creating a fence beam for mortar locating radars, described in Chapter 6, or sometimes in air defence radars as a tracking aid. In Figure 4.19 the signal to be transmitted is input to the feed horn to create a diverging beam within the parallel plate waveguide. This waveguide is simply two parallel metal sheets separated by a gap equivalent to the feed waveguide height. This diverging beam bounces off a parabolic reflector located between the plates to form a parallel beam in the lower parallel plate section. This lower section acts as a feed for the rotating conical cylinder. The inner cylinder is smaller than the outer jacket so that the wave can pass through the gap between them. The baffles shown in Figure 4.19b force the wave coming from the feed and reflector to pass upward between the cylinders. The inner cylinder is split and a further baffle forces the

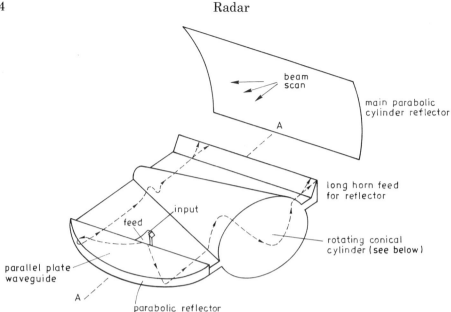

(a)

(b)

Fig. 4.19   Foster scanner: (a) scanner details, (b) cross section of AA

wave to propagate down the slot formed by the two halves. Further baffles make the
wave exit into the parallel plate waveguide and hence toward the feed for the main
parabolic reflector. The inner cylinder is rotating at high speed with baffles
designed not to interfere with the rotation. When the cylinder centre slot is
horizontal the wave passes through the system without deviation round the
cylinder. A beam coming straight out from the main reflector results. When the
cylinder has rotated, as in Figure 4.19b, the wave must pass the extra distance
around the cylinder. At the thin end of the cone this extra distance is less than at
the fat end and this difference in path length causes the beam emerging from the
feed to point slightly to one side. As the cylinder rotates the beam direction moves
progressively sideways until eventually, as the cylinder slot lines up with the feeds
again, the beam suddenly jumps back to the straight out direction. In this way the
cylinder rotation results in a fast horizontal beam scan.

Adaptive Antennas

The radar on the battlefield is likely to be subjected to jamming or other sources of noise and the computer control of a phased array can be used to reduce the damaging effect of interference. When used in this way the array is said to be adaptive in that it alters the radiation pattern to place nulls in jammer directions. It can even do this during operation, which is important if the jamming environment changes during the battle.

To understand how an adaptive antenna works, the simple example of a null steering antenna is now described. A null steering capability can be added to a conventional antenna simply by adding a small secondary antenna, as shown in Figure 4.20. The radiation patterns involved are shown in Figure 4.21. A jammer

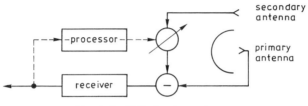

FIG. 4.20   Null steering antenna

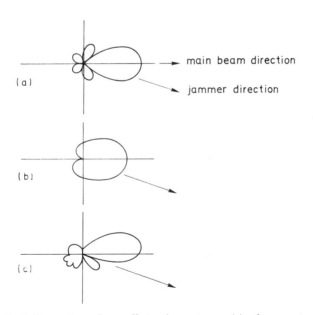

FIG. 4.21   Radiation patterns in a null steering antenna: (a) primary antenna pattern, (b) secondary antenna pattern, (c) combined pattern

signal is strongly received by the primary antenna. It is also received by the secondary antenna. If the amplitude of the secondary output is adjusted so that it is equal to the jammer signal received by the primary, when the two are subtracted, the combined radiation pattern will effectively have a null in the jammer

direction, and the receiver will give a clear unjammed output. If the phase of the
secondary signal is also controlled, the null can be made to move around the
antenna or, more importantly, the null can be stationary as the antenna either
mechanically rotates or is electronically scanned. In this case the reflector shown
in Figure 4.20 can be replaced by a phased array.

One key problem in adaptive null steering antennas is how to control the phase
and amplitude, or complex weighting as it is called, of the secondary antenna. If
the direction of the jamming is known, the weight can be calculated. However, in
practice this is not usually the case. If the jamming signal has a characteristic
signature that can be detected at the output of the receiver, the weight can simply
be varied until the jamming is reduced. Usually things are not so simple, and the
jamming will appear as noise. In this case the arrangement of Figure 4.22 can be

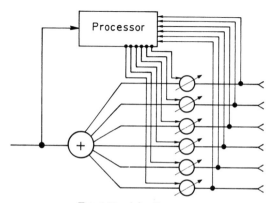

FIG. 4.22   Adaptive array

used. An adaptive array is shown but the principle can be applied to the primary
and secondary arrangement of Figure 4.20. Here information about both the
signals on each element and the combined signal are fed to the processor. The
processor is arranged to minimise the combined output whilst maintaining a given
array gain in the required direction again by varying the complex weights of each
element signal before it goes to the combiner. This in effect minimises the
influence of noise from whatever direction it is received.

In current systems both null steering and fully adaptive systems can be seen. A
limitation of the null steering arrangement is that only one jammer can be nulled.
To increase its capability more secondary antennas are used. The many feedback
paths of the fully adaptive system give much greater capability but need a much
larger and faster processor.

Multiple Beam Antennas

A conventional phased array moves the beam through the area to be covered in a
sequential way and step the beam from direction to direction. Many radar systems
have the capability of forming antenna beams in several directions at the same

time and these are called multiple beam systems. The arrangement is shown diagrammatically in Figure 4.23. This could represent, for example, the antenna of a 3D surveillance radar with height finding capability by monopulse comparison on the several elevation beams, as described in Chapter 3. The array elements are connected to a beamformer: each output from it corresponds to a single beam. Each beam output may then have its own receiver or a single receiver may be switched between the outputs.

The beamformer may use many different technologies, such as an interconnected microwave circuit, a microwave lens, an intermediate frequency circuit, or even be implemented using a digital processor. In the latter case each array element output has to have its own receiver, the output of which is sampled and converted to a digital bit stream.

Digital Processing and Displays

Digital Processing

Many radar functions, for example filtering and signal detection by thresholding, are performed by using analogue circuits. In an analogue circuit the signals are continuously varying voltages or currents. Capacitors, inductors, diodes and transistors are typical components in such circuits. However, if the signal is sampled sufficiently fast, that is at twice the highest frequency, and each sample height coded, a digital bit stream can be created. Processing of the bit stream by a computer can then simulate many of the functions performed by analogue processing.

The importance of digital processing lies in the fact that computer circuits can be made using only transistors or diodes, without large capacitors or inductors, and this allows very high levels of integration. Thus high capacity processors can be made on single chips typically a few millimetres square. Figure 4.24 shows a typical digital integrated circuit. The key limitation in digital processing is computer speed. Many personal computers have a clock rate of 1–10 MHz; special processing chips are now being produced with speeds greater than 1 GHz. When it is remembered that most radars have operating frequencies in excess of 1 GHz it is clear that, at the moment, digital processing cannot be done on the signals coming from the antenna. However, processing of the intermediate frequency signals is possible and processing at baseband is now widely used. Thus some mixture of analogue and digital processing is likely to be found in radars for some time to come.

As an example of a digital process an FFT is now described. A Fourier Transform of a time waveform is its frequency spectrum, so the FFT is a key element in digital filtering. The time waveform is sampled at, for example, eight points, as shown in Figure 4.25. The height of each sample is measured to form an equivalent coded bitstream. The blocks of bits representing each sample height are then mixed to form a new set of eight numbers. In the mixing process the first number is added to the fifth one to form a new first. The new second number is the old second plus the old sixth and so on. However, the new fifth number is the old first plus the old fifth multiplied by ω^4 and so on. ω is a complex number and effectively introduces a phase change. This regrouping process is repeated as shown four times with the

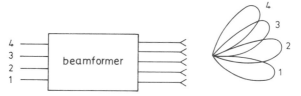

FIG. 4.23   Multiple beam array

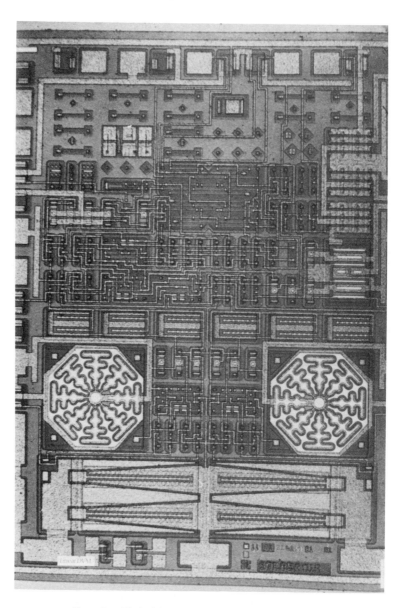

FIG. 4.24   Digital integrated circuit *(Courtesy of CIT)*

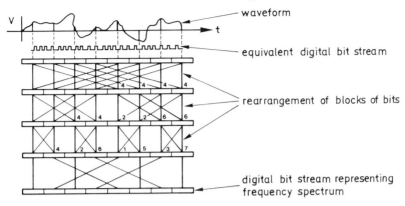

waveform

equivalent digital bit stream

rearrangement of blocks of bits

digital bit stream representing
frequency spectrum

FIG. 4.25   Fast Fourier Transform (FFT) processing (each block of bits represents one
sample height)

numbers representing powers of ω. The last set of eight numbers is effectively the
frequency spectrum of the input waveform. Filtering can be achieved by selecting
one number from the eight or any group of them. It can be appreciated that many
add and multiply operations must be performed to complete the FFT and, to limit
this, as few as say 32 or 64 samples of a waveform may be taken. Built in test
equipment (BITE) is an important radar capability that has evolved through the
use of digital processing. It is encountered by the operator of a modern radar, who
upon switching on, is informed on the display that the radar is running self
checking routines. From this point of view it is seen as an operator confidence
booster. However, much more can be done: for example, if a fault develops during
operation the user will be told the nature of the fault and whether normal
operation can continue. Information on fault type will also greatly ease the job of
those repairing the equipment.

   Both digital and analogue circuits can be checked by BITE. Correct operation of
the digital circuits can be confirmed by running simple software exercises with
known results. Software integrity is measured by calculating a checksum on the
code. The number of digits in all or part of the program are known and if the count
is different, the code is obviously corrupted. Such tests can be done before and
periodically during radar operation. This form of BITE is based on an expected
response to a given stimulus. However, testing of analogue circuits is mainly by
monitoring of voltage, current and power levels at various points and is applied
continuously. For example, a directional coupler is inserted between the
transmitter and antenna to measure the power output of the oscillator and also the
power reflected from the antenna. Many antenna faults result in a mismatch and
hence power reflection. Power supply monitoring and thermal cutouts are other
examples of analogue BITE.

Displays

   Early radar displays consisted of a cathode ray tube, such as that shown in
Figure 4.26, and these are still widely used today. The received echoes can be
displayed in a variety of ways. In Figure 4.27a the display is arranged so that range

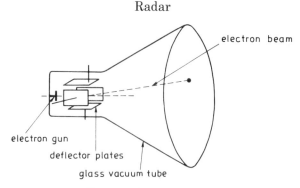

FIG. 4.26   Cathode ray tube

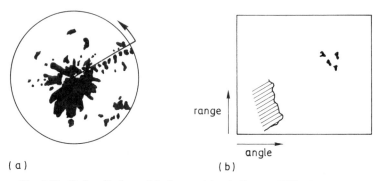

(a)   (b)

FIG. 4.27   Radar displays: (a) plan position indicator (PPI), (b) B scope

from the radar is distance from the screen centre and target bearing is measured
around this. Such a PPI gives a clear indication of the disposition of targets around
the radar which is effectively located at screen centre. The screen is refreshed in
time with the antenna rotation so that a bright bar appears to move round the
screen as shown. This display is widely used in surveillance and ship navigation
radars. If the antenna is scanning a limited sector, the display of Figure 4.27b may
be used: the linear scales for angle and range are used and this allows good
resolution of near in targets which is difficult with PPI.

   Traditionally the output from the radar receiver was put to the display through
appropriate circuits to give the correct display type, namely PPI, B scope, etc.
However, the advent of digital processing has allowed a far more flexible display
arrangement to be used. A conventional raster scan is used on the display but the
display type is generated in software, creating what is called synthetic display.
This allows additional data to be displayed including alphanumeric characters
associated with the state of the radar, display and target classification or
identification. Furthermore, some degree of threat assessment can be incorporated
with target display by priority and this can greatly reduce operator fatigue.

   Other display technologies are also being incorporated into modern radars, such
as electroluminescent panels and liquid crystal displays. These seem appropriate
to lightweight radars as they are themselves more compact and require small
power supplies.

5

Battlefield Surveillance Radar

The Requirement for Battlefield Surveillance Radar

The requirement for timely information about enemy deployments and movements is vital for the battlefield commander. Radar plays an important role in this need as it provides day and night surveillance in all weather out to long ranges. There are two distinct types of BSR. Short range radars operate out to 30 or 40 km, may be manportable or vehicle mounted depending on range, and may be used for surveillance of moving objects, target acquisition and correction of fall of shot. Radars for surveillance beyond the front line at ranges in excess of 100 km are carried in aircraft or helicopters and are able to detect moving targets or to give radar photographs. Both of these types are currently in use or being proposed by many nations.

The key technical problem with battlefield surveillance is that of ground clutter. Both short and long range types are looking for targets on the ground, and the ground return may well be larger than from the target. Two solutions to this problem are possible. First, Doppler processing may be used. Any radial movement of the target allows it to be picked out of the return from the stationary ground. Hence as most targets will have some component of movement away from or towards the radar, they will be seen. The second technique is to form a high resolution picture of the ground return using an SAR. If the resolution is sufficiently high, the targets may be visually identified from the picture whether they are moving or not. Detailed explanations of these techniques have been given in Chapter 3. The application to battlefield surveillance is now presented.

Short Range Battlefield Surveillance Radar

Introduction

Modern short range BSRs are required to be able to detect the presence of targets out to ranges up to 40 km, with a probability of detection of typically 80% or more and with a false alarm rate of not more than, for example, one in 15 min. The type of targets encountered comprises single men, groups of men, light vehicles, tracked vehicles, helicopters and fall of shot. The requirement for tracking projectiles is carried out by the specialised radars described in Chapter 8. The required resolution and accuracy depend on what other weapons the radar is being used to cue, if any; the link between fall of shot accuracy and gun circular error probable (CEP) is self-evident. Minimum size and weight are needed, coupled with simple operation and some resistance to countermeasures.

Returns from these types of target may be many tens of decibels below the ground clutter and thus Doppler processing is the primary technique used in such radars. Figure 5.1 shows how the moving target signal at frequency $f_c + f_d$ plus the

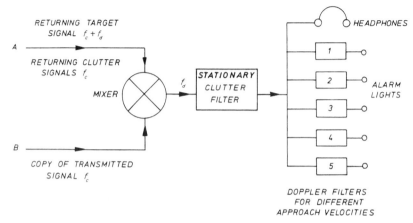

FIG. 5.1   Principle of Doppler signal processing

signal from the surrounding clutter at frequency f_c is mixed in the receiver with a copy of the transmitted signal at f_c. The mixer output is the difference of these two frequencies, that is the Doppler signal at f_d. This passes through the stationary clutter filter tuned to pass all likely target Doppler frequencies whilst rejecting clutter from stationary and slow moving objects such as the ground or wind blown vegetation. The target Doppler can then be applied to a series of Doppler filters to estimate the approaching or receding velocity and hence to a display of some form or to the headphones, so that the operator can classify the target. There are two methods of obtaining the copy of the transmitted signal, illustrated in Figure 5.2. It has been noted that the radar will illuminate not only the target but also an area of surrounding stationary clutter. Hence the return from the target area contains not only the signal at $f_c + f_d$ but also f_c, as shown in Figure 5.2a. If this alone is applied to mixer, the Doppler signal will be obtained. This method is called clutter reference radar. It is relatively simple to implement and was used in early BSRs such as the Marconi ZB298. However, it is less efficient at extracting signals from clutter than the method shown in Figure 5.2b. Here the copy of the transmitted signal is literally taken from the transmitter. This is called an internally coherent radar and current radars using this method can see targets that are as much as 40 dB below the clutter signal. Most modern BSRs use this method. However, if the radar is to be used from a moving vehicle, the internally coherent type must be modified to take account of the vehicle velocity whereas clutter reference types will work unmodified.

Target classification is an attractive feature of these radars. When the Doppler

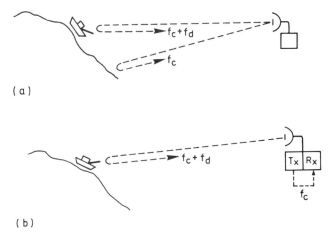

(a)

(b)

FIG. 5.2   Types of Doppler radar: (a) clutter reference radar, (b) internally coherent
radar

frequency is converted directly into an audio signal the note from the various types
of target is distinct and, although automatic classification is some way off, human
operators can recognise them with only limited training. Table 5.1 lists the
characteristic note of the various target types. The low pitched rumbling of a
moving person sometimes resembles the sound of a base drum accompanied by a
low pitched whine. Each thump corresponds to a step. A group of moving men
produces a similar sound but each step is not distinct. The pitch of a vehicle sound
is proportional to its speed. The type of overtones can be used to differentiate
between wheeled and tracked vehicles.

   Two primary techniques have been used to allow range measurement in the
radars described later in this chapter. Most use conventional pulse techniques and
are thus pulse Doppler radars. However, the American BSRs built by RCA use
pseudo-noise coded (PNC) transmissions. This method requires lower peak
transmitted power than pulse Doppler radars and hence good immunity to ESM.

Typical Radar Characteristics

Frequency of Operation

Targets must be detectable out to the specified range in all specified weather
conditions. The transmitted power required must be minimised to ensure
maximum operating time using battery supplies, whilst the antenna size must be
minimised to aid portability within the constraints of the required radar
resolution. The frequency selection is a complicated parametric study involving
these and other factors. The typical frequency range chosen is 10–20 GHz, and
components are readily available in this range. The mean radiated power is of the
order of a few watts with peak power of a few kilowatts.

PRF

   The PRF is chosen so that the radar has no blind speeds for vehicles travelling at

TABLE 5.1

Doppler Signature of Typical Battlefield Targets

Target type	Doppler sound
Wind blown foliage	Low pitched random rumbling
Moving person	Periodic low pitched rumbling
Slow moving vehicle	Even rumbling of varying pitch with synchronised overtones
Fast moving vehicle	Even whine of varying pitch with synchronised overtones
Tracked vehicle	Even rumble or whine with synchronised overtones changing pitch together

the maximum velocity envisaged. For a maximum speed of 25 m/s the maximum Doppler frequency in a 10 GHz radar is 1.66 kHz. The PRF must be higher than this and values of 2 kHz and upwards are not uncommon.

Resolution

For a range resolution of, for example, 25 m the pulse length must be 0.16 μs and such pulses can be generated. It makes the radar blind to a minimum distance of 25 m.

The antenna size is fixed by the frequency of operation and the required angular resolution. For a resolution of 50 m at 1 km, which is equivalent to 50 mils or 2.86°, the antenna size must be about 0.7 m at 10 GHz or 0.35 m at 20 GHz. The antenna beamwidth in elevation is sometimes taken as twice this, so an antenna twice as wide as it is high results.

Doppler processing is carried out in modern radars by digital FFT. The Doppler waveform may be digitised at 50 or more points and the FFT algorithm will produce a frequency spectrum composed of an equivalent number of points. Clutter rejection and target velocity measurement are then performed on this spectrum.

Overall Characteristics

An overall block diagram of a typical BSR is shown in Figure 5.3. The precise form of the radio frequency (RF) components such as generator, amplifier, receiver and antenna may differ between models but the techniques are as described in preceding chapters. A precise clock is required to synchronise the transmitter, receiver and processing unit. The processed data is output to the man-machine interface in a variety of forms. A control panel will also be provided to allow the operator to control such things as antenna position and scan range, transmitter frequency and the type of data displayed. As the antenna has a relatively narrow beam a rigid tripod is required that incorporates the antenna drive servos. Usually the RF assembly is mounted with or close to the antenna on the tripod whilst the display and control panel may be remoted a safe distance away by cable. The radar may be powered by portable or vehicle batteries. In vehicle mounted installations the antenna and RF unit will be mounted on top with the display and control panel within the vehicle.

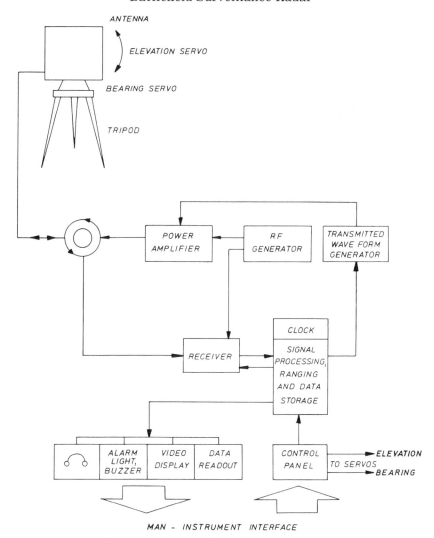

ANTENNA

ELEVATION SERVO

BEARING SERVO

TRIPOD

POWER AMPLIFIER

RF GENERATOR

TRANSMITTED WAVE FORM GENERATOR

CLOCK

RECEIVER

SIGNAL PROCESSING, RANGING AND DATA STORAGE

ALARM LIGHT, BUZZER

VIDEO DISPLAY

DATA READOUT

CONTROL PANEL

TO SERVOS

ELEVATION

BEARING

MAN - INSTRUMENT INTERFACE

FIG. 5.3   Typical pulse Doppler battlefield surveillance radar (BSR)

Important New Technology

Technology has advanced rapidly in the area of BSR in recent years since, for example, the inception of the UK radar ZB298. Two areas of advance should be mentioned here. The advent of digital processing chips has meant that the control of radar functions by software programs is now possible. One important advantage of this is the current inclusion of BITE. It allows the radar to diagnose its own faults down to printed circuit board level, consequently faster servicing and greater availability is achieved. Another area of improvement is in display technology. The radars described below use CRO, electroluminescent, liquid crystal displays or other types. On these it is possible, again using digital processing, to create a synthetic display that is 'user friendly'. Figure 5.4 shows a

FIG. 5.4   Typical battlefield surveillance radar display *(Courtesy Thorn-EMI Ltd)*

typical example. A sector scan is shown. Targets are clearly indicated by large symbols and information such as target speed or direction may also be given. Next to the sector display, an alphanumeric section can give, for example, operating menus, allowing easy selection of radar function, target co-ordinates, battery condition and other data.

Examples of Current BSRs

Many varieties of BSR are currently available, with a wide range of specific capabilities. However, it is obvious that many features are common and this is perhaps not surprising since in many cases similar requirements are being met with similar technology. Some of them are described here to highlight important features. The radars use pulse Doppler techniques unless otherwise stated.

Figure 5.5 shows the *RASIT-E* produced by LMT Radio Professionale. It can be seen that it takes the form shown in the block diagram of Figure 5.3 of a reflector antenna and the RF unit mounted on a tripod with a remote control box. Figure 5.6 shows the radar mounted on a vehicle. In addition the radar can be mounted on a mast. The manufacturers give the following performance characteristics. The control unit contains an integral power converter to allow a variety of supplies to be used. When run from a 100 Ahr 24 V vehicle battery, endurance of longer than

FIG. 5.5   RASIT radar *(Courtesy LMT Radio Professionale)*

15 hours is expected. The quoted range performance is up to 23 km for pedestrians, up to 32 km for light vehicles, up to 40 km for trucks, and 20–40 km for helicopters. The signals are displayed on a CRO. A radar image in azimuth and range of the clutter or slow or fast moving targets can be shown. Four operating modes are possible. In normal surveillance mode any 20 km interval out to 40 km can be displayed over any desired scan angle. When a target of interest appears the operator selects it on the screen using a cursor and switches to acquisition and identification mode. The target co-ordinates are displayed and the target Doppler signature can be heard in the headphones. It can then be tracked. The zone surveillance and accurate acquisition modes are similar to those above but cover only a 2.5×2.5 km^2. Map co-ordination is also possible using an add on plotting table capable of accommodating 1 : 50,000 or 1 : 250,000 scale maps. The radar PRF

FIG. 5.6   RASIT mounted on STEYR armoured vehicle *(Courtesy LMT Radio Professionale)*

is 3,660 Hz, the pulse width is 0.33 μs and 3 W mean and 3 kW peak RF power are transmitted. Radiated polarisation is normally vertical, although circular can be selected to help suppress rain clutter. Electronic counter countermeasures (ECCM) include several selectable frequencies and an adjustable sensitivity control.

Many of these features are possessed by the MSTAR radar, shown in Figure 5.7, produced by Thorn EMI Ltd. The overall shape is similar although the display and control console use an electroluminescent panel and a membrane type keyboard capable of operation by a user wearing an NBC suit. The manufacturers quote an overall weight of about 28 kg. The MSTAR radar has a fall of shot capability, in which a 1 km^2 area is displayed. Returns from the spoil thrown up by the exploding shell are detected and the co-ordinates can be relayed to the gun for aiming correction.

Figure 5.8 shows a short range BSR, the RB-12 from Thomson CSF. The manufacturers quote the following characteristics. It has a range capability of 5 km for vehicles and 2 km for men, with a location accuracy of $\pm 1°$ (± 18 mils) in azimuth and ± 10 m in range. The display is a liquid crystal with an associated 20 character keyboard. It operates in the J band and has five selectable frequencies. Transmitting a mean RF power of 35 mW its dc power consumption is 15 W giving an operating time of the order of 10 hours. The all up weight is 28 kg.

The AN/PPS series contains a range of small radars made by RCA in the United States. In general terms capabilities are similar to the radar described above

FIG. 5.7   MSTAR radar *(Courtesy Thorn-EMI Ltd)*

ranging from 1 km for vehicles for a small 4.5 kg version to 10 km for a 20 kg type. These use the PNC technique for range measurement coupled with conventional Doppler processing for clutter rejection. Figure 5.9 shows a block diagram of how such a radar works. The PNC is used to modulate the transmitted signal. The received signal is decoded by comparing it to a time delayed copy of the transmitted code. If this delay is the same as the time taken for the signal to propagate to and return from the target, the two codes line up and a strong signal is received. The operating procedure is to set the radar to scan automatically the required sector with a wide open range resolution of 0.5 km. When a target is obtained the scan is stopped; the resolution is reduced to 25 m by increasing the

FIG. 5.8   RB-12 radar *(Courtesy LMT Radio Professionale)*

clock rate and the delay adjusted to measure the range. The audio output of target is thus available to the operator.

Soviet BSRs are shown in Figures 5.10 and 5.11. Again it can be seen that the overall size and shape are similar to the radars described above.

Airborne Battlefield Surveillance Radar

Introduction

When surveillance out to ranges of 100 km and greater is required the curvature of the earth's surface dictates that an elevated platform must be used. Many types of platform have been considered for this role such as satellites, aircraft, both manned and unmanned tethered platforms, balloons, kites, shells or missiles. Radar surveillance from satellite is now a reality with high quality pictures of

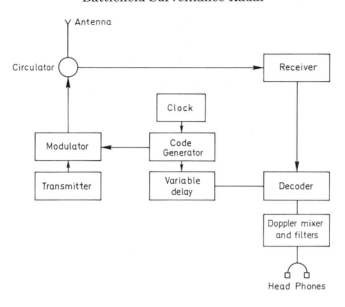

FIG. 5.9   Operation of pseudo-noise code (CNR) radar

FIG. 5.10   Soviet battlefield surveillance radar *(Crown copyright/MOD photograph)*

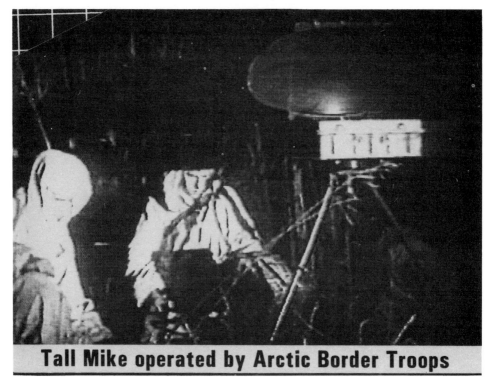

Tall Mike operated by Arctic Border Troops

FIG. 5.11   Soviet battlefield surveillance radar *(Crown copyright/MOD photograph)*

large areas being available using the SAR technique. However, the usefulness of this data is limited for tactical use by the frequency of the satellite orbit. The use of unmanned and manned aircraft can be divided into those which fly over or relatively close to the target and those that stand well back and use long range sensors. The former are generally non real-time systems, but will provide data with very good resolution and accuracy using photographic infra red and sideways looking radar sensors. The latter, known as stand off radar (SOR) systems, will in general have poorer accuracy and in addition to providing information about enemy movements may be used to cue an unmanned sensor flying over the area of interest to provide precise targeting. It is the SOR concept that is described here.

A radar must be used if SOR is to give long range and all weather operation. In principle any airborne vehicle can be used. However, in practice, as the radar payload may weigh up to 500 kg, either a helicopter or manned aircraft is necessary. For observation beyond the front line, the aircraft height may be 500–10,000 m at distances 10–80 km behind the front line. Although some of the signal processing may take place within the aircraft, a ground control station is likely to be used, where signal processing, display and analysis take place.

Principles of SOR

The concept of an SOR is shown in Figure 5.12. The elevated radar observes an area of ground. The size of this area determines the radar resolution. The

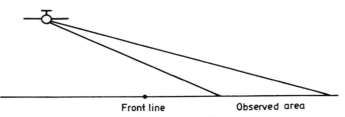

Front line   Observed area

FIG. 5.12   Stand off radar (SOR) concept

important parameters here are the antenna beamwidths, ϕ_{az} and ϕ_{el} in the azimuth and elevation directions, respectively, and the elevation angle, θ_e. The area A is given by:

$$A = R\phi_{az}\frac{R\phi_{el}}{\sin\theta_e}$$

where R is the range and ϕ_{az} and ϕ_{el} are in radians. If a pulse radar were used, as is generally the case, the situation would be modified, as shown in Figure 5.13. The

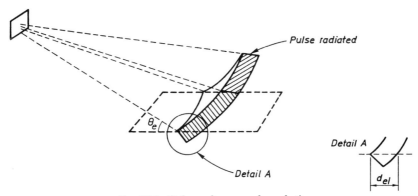

Pulse radiated

Detail A

Detail A

d_{el}

FIG. 5.13   Pulse radar ground resolution

area drawn out on the ground by the pulse at any instant in time, known as the resolution cell, is given by:

$$A = R\phi_{az}\frac{c\tau}{2\cos\theta_e}$$

where c is the velocity of light and τ is the pulse length. The azimuth beamwidth is determined by the wavelength λ and antenna width L_{az} so that A is now given by:

$$A = \frac{R\lambda}{L_{az}}\frac{c\tau}{2\cos\theta_e}$$

This area primarily determines the radar resolution and accuracy. To improve these A must be small. In this case, however, A will not cover the area of interest and some scanning must take place. As the radar is mounted in a moving vehicle which is subject to sudden movement due to turbulence and other effects, some degree of automatic antenna stabilisation linked to the scanning mechanism is usually required.

To achieve ranges out to 100 km and more together with good resolution a frequency in the NATO I band may be chosen.

Stand off Radar Resolution

The radar resolution is a key feature of SOR, determining whether conventional or synthetic aperture techniques are to be used. Assuming a range requirement of 100 km, a wavelength of 30 mm (corresponding to 10 GHz) and an antenna width of 1 m, the azimuth resolution is approximately 3 km. For a radar with a $\tau = 0.1$ μs pulse width at an elevation of $\theta_e = 2°$, the down range resolution is about 15 m. Thus although the down range resolution is adequate, that in the cross range direction is poor and will not allow good discrimination of land features such as roads, or military targets such as vehicles or aircraft on the ground. In this case the raw radar return is of little use and clutter rejection techniques such as MTI are used. This means that land features are suppressed whilst targets moving radially to the radar will be displayed with a resolution as indicated above. Thus it is likely that massed formations of moving vehicles or columns or vehicles on roads will be identified. Accurate knowledge of the radar antenna direction and position in space are required to allow map relation.

Operation of an MTI radar from a moving platform gives rise to some differences in the processing when compared to a stationary radar. Figure 5.14 shows that

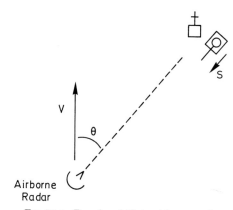

FIG. 5.14   Doppler shift in airborne radar

there will be a Doppler shift from a stationary clutter target due to the radar movement. There is an additional Doppler shift from the moving target and the processing has to differentiate between these two shifts. Furthermore, the Doppler due to the radar motion is dependent on the radar look angle θ. Hence knowledge of θ and radar speed are necessary. Some radar scanning may also be needed to keep the beam on the required area if the look angle approaches 90°. Additionally, clutter returns through the sidelobes will have a different Doppler shift to those in the main beam.

The radar cross range resolution can be greatly reduced by using the SAR technique, described in detail in Chapter 3. There it was shown that the azimuth resolution d_{az} is given by:

$$d_{az} = L_{az}/2$$

and for this case $d_{az} = 0.5$ m. Thus, theoretically, very fine resolution can be achieved enabling discrimination of land features and military targets. Such a technique gives a radar picture as shown in Figure 5.15. Roads, hedges and buildings can be clearly seen and by comparing scenes taken over a period of time movement of vehicles can be established.

Target Imaging

Target imaging is done in an MTI radar by range gating and by antenna rotation. In an SAR the antenna is fixed and the image is created by range gating and by flying the aircraft smoothly down a track parallel to the target area to form a swath defined by the sideways looking radar.

For conventional radars, a rotating scan in which the antenna rotates through 360° may be used but this requires mounting the antenna above or below the aircraft. Alternatively, a sector scan of less than 200° might be adequate for an aircraft looking forward over the front line. Relatively slow aircraft or helicopters can be used if desired. SAR processing is dependent on the aircraft flying a straight course and this implies a higher speed for best resolution. The aircraft lateral position must be maintained to less than a millimetre or some form of motion compensation must be used. This takes a form similar to inertial navigation systems. Typically, a speed of 200–300 knots with motion compensation will give resolutions down to a few metres. The swath width is determined by the antenna design and power considerations. Typical swath widths are up to 20–30 km.

SAR can also be applied to conventional radars operating in slower aircraft by synthesising a fixed length of aperture, and here resolutions of about 25 m at 100 km range can be expected. This is called Doppler beam sharpening (DBS) and is frequently used in forward squint mode SAR. An enhanced image of a selected small view can be obtained which can be superimposed on the conventional MTI radar image.

It is possible that MTI may also be applied by independent simultaneous processing to SAR systems to further aid image clarity. It should be noted that cross range displacements in position for moving targets occur in SAR and a combined MTI/SAR system may help to remove these ambiguities.

Displays

Using a conventional MTI radar with sector scan only moving targets would be detected. These could be displayed in the form of a printout of location, size, direction of movement, speed and time of detection. Alternatively, the targets

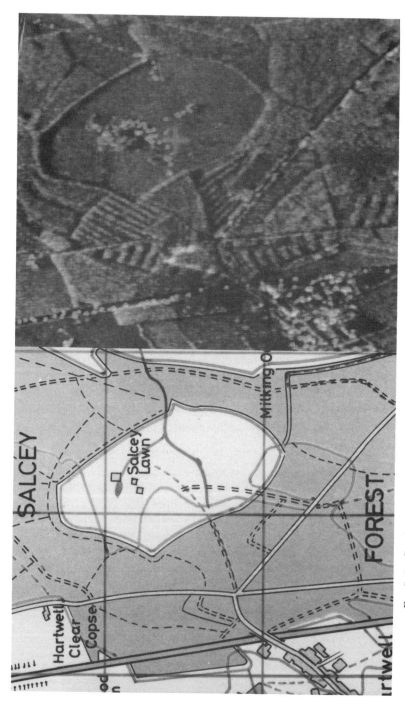

Fig. 5.15 Synthetic aperture radar (SAR) image (SAR image right, map left) (*Courtesy Thorn-EMI Ltd*)

could be displayed on a visual display unit (VDU) with internal map relation or an overlaid map facility. Accuracy may be of the order of 100 m at 50 km for armoured fighting vehicles (AFVs) and 150 m at 80 km for groups of AFVs.

Current SAR systems produce pictures similar to Figure 5.15 over large areas and hence require interpretation by skilled operators, which takes considerable time. However, the use of SAR at a tactical level could target small areas of, say, 10 km × 10 km in a short time and require modest interpretation.

It is likely that high speed digital processors may allow the SAR processing to be done in the aircraft in near real time. This will speed the information flow which may then be limited by the interpretation time.

Practical Systems

Airborne BSR is a relatively new requirement and there are few practical systems in service. Figures 5.16 and 5.17 show two solutions being examined in the

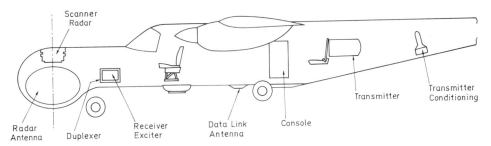

FIG. 5.16   Pilatus Britten-Norman *Defender* aircraft equipped with long range battlefield surveillance radar *(Courtesy Thorn EMI Ltd)*

United Kingdom by Thorn EMI in the ASTOR (airborne/stand off radar) programme. The Pilatus Britten-Norman *Defender* aircraft in Figure 5.16 is being equipped with an MTI radar based on the existing *Skymaster* radar. It is intended to fly this aircraft at about 1,000 m altitude, relatively close to the front line to give a range of over 100 km beyond. Further range and higher resolution is expected from the *Canberra* mounted radar, shown in Figure 5.17, that is intended to use SAR with a combined MTI mode, operating at about 20,000 m altitude. Figure 5.18 shows the *Orchidée* (Observatoire Radar Cohérent Héliporte d'Investigation des Eléments Ennemis) system. The 3.5 m long radar antenna is mounted below the body of a *Super Puma* helicopter. Operation altitude is similar to the ASTOR *Defender* aircraft and range capability is also likely to be similar. The US solution employs a multi-mode combined MTI/SAR radar mounted in a modified Boeing 707 aircraft flying at about 10,000 m altitude. The radar employs a phased array and in addition to having a surveillance role can be employed for weapons guidance. Several cathode ray tube (CRT) displays and control stations may be mounted in the aircraft.

In all these examples, secure command and data links with the ground stations are necessary. The use of several ground stations per aircraft will enhance the

FIG. 5.17 *Canberra* fitted with prototype SAR *(Courtesy Thorn-EMI Ltd)*

FIG. 5.18 *Super Puma* carrying *Orchidée* system *(Courtesy LCTAR, Thomson CSF)*

system flexibility. As these radars will have great tactical value they are likely to be attacked both electronically and physically. The amount of ECCM that can be carried is of course limited by the aircraft payload capabilities. Specific details of radar electronic warfare are considered in Chapter 9.

6

Weapon Locating Radars

The Role of a Weapon Locating Radar

The purpose of a weapon locating radar (WLR) is to detect the launch of an enemy projectile or missile and to establish a segment of the trajectory of the projectile of sufficient length and positional accuracy to enable a computer to determine the location of the launcher. Counter action may then be taken against the gun or launcher. This technique is known as back track location or back extrapolation because the computer follows back along the measured portion of the projectile path to the point where it intersects the ground.

The main type of weapons against which WLRs are directed are mortars, free flight rockets, and guns, which may operate in the high angle or low angle mode.

WLRs may also have some value against guided missiles if they can track the missile shortly after launch, but the back extrapolation to the launcher can be properly calculated only if the missile trajectory is held in the computer memory. This is seldom possible for guided missiles except for the early part of their flight.

General Technical Requirements

The radar 'target' is the enemy projectile which will have a small RCS and may be very fast moving. The target may appear at any time, usually without warning, so the radar must cover the whole possible volume of target space in the acquisition mode, either with a high repetition rate scan beam, or with a floodlight antenna system. Despite this requirement it is desirable that the transmitter should have as small a signature as possible, in order to avoid location by enemy ESM units. Weather backscatter may be severe and ground clutter may be a major problem, particularly in the case of low angle projectiles moving close to the ground. Good angle, range and perhaps Doppler resolution is therefore essential. The accuracy of track must match the requirement for location of the enemy launch system. In some cases the enemy may be a number of launch units within a small area of ground. The WLR might then be required to establish the mean centre of the enemy deployment.

The Principle of Back Track Location

The concept of launcher location by back extrapolation along the trajectory is shown in Figure 6.1. The WLR, at an accurately known position on the map,

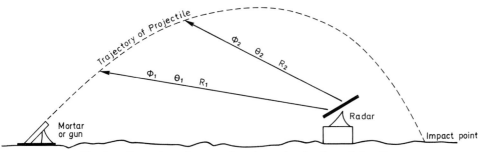

FIG. 6.1   Operation of weapon locating radar: back track location

detects, tracks and measures the position of the enemy projectile at two or more points on its path. If the system is to be used against different types of weapon or mortar using several choices of charge, the time interval between the two location points is also measured. In Figure 6.1 ϕ_1, θ_1, and R_1 represent the azimuth, elevation and range from the WLR of the lower position of the projectile, whilst ϕ_2, θ_2 and R_2 represent the upper position. This data, together with the weapon trajectory in the WLR computer memory, enable the computer to find the point at which the trajectory meets the ground, which is the location of the gun or mortar. The trajectory of the enemy projectile may be obtained from range tables, if these are available. If they are not known, an assumed trajectory must be provided to the computer. Mortar bombs move at subsonic speeds, so little error will be incurred in neglecting air resistance and calculating on the basis of a parabolic projectile path. It should be noted that the expected point of impact of the projectile may also be determined, though to a lesser degree of accuracy, than that of the launch point because of the much longer length of the extrapolation required.

Figure 6.2 shows that the computer must also have available terrain height information if location error is to be minimised. This may be seen by considering

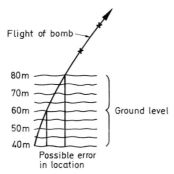

FIG. 6.2   Location error due to launch height

the following. The operational information needed is the map reference of the mortar. Initially it may be assumed that the mortar and the WLR are sited on a flat plane with no height difference between them. In this case simple back tracking will give the correct map position where the trajectory intersects the ground plane. However, if the mortar is sited, for example, on a hill 50 m higher than the ground plane on which the radar rests and it is assumed that the projectile is fired at an angle of 45° directly towards the radar, simple back tracking will place the mortar on the ground plane 50 m further from the WLR. This would give a horizontal error of 50 m if no terrain height data is available. The computation for the general case demands a 3D geometrical model of the relative position of the radar and the mortar and the height characteristics of the local terrain. The height data and the radar location may be fed to the computer from military maps and navigation instruments when the radar is sited. When the mortar data is obtained the computer can use the terrain information to correct the initial simple determination of the mortar map reference.

Figure 6.3 shows how ambiguities in weapon location can occur if the projectile follows a path close to rising ground during the early part of its flight. The lower

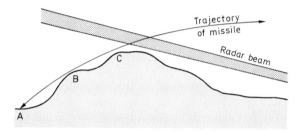

FIG. 6.3   Ambiguities due to terrain profile

radar beam, shown passing over a crest in the ground, obtains the first fix of the projectile. A higher beam, not shown in the diagram, will obtain the upper point of the trajectory. The mortar bomb path is shown originating at point A but almost touching the ground at points B and C. It will be seen that a small error in the calculation of the trajectory will result in B or C being obtained as the position of the weapon.

It will also be clear from these diagrams that the accuracy of location may be more readily obtained for high angle fire systems because the trajectory will meet the ground plane more nearly vertically and will thus produce a more precise point of intersection.

Practical Systems

Early mortar location equipment and current radars were made using radars designed for other roles. This met with limited success, due mainly to the slow beam scan rate of available mechanical antennas. The development of the Foster scanner and the frequency scan antenna led to the introduction of the first true WLR. Improved versions of this type of equipment are still in service, for the location of mortars, but as explained later, gun location demands more elaborate technology.

Table 6.1 gives a set of parameters for a typical but hypothetical mortar location radar. Table 6.2 gives a range calculation. The following factors control the technical characteristics designed into such a WLR:

TABLE 6.1

Typical Parameters of a Mortar Locating Radar

Max range	15 km
Min range	700 m
Scanned sector	45°
Radar carrier frequency	10 GHz
Peak power	100 kW
Mean power	$1\frac{1}{2}$ kW
Time required for location	15 s
Weight of equipment on two wheel trailer	1,200 kg

TABLE 6.2

Radar Range Calculation for a Typical Mortar Locating Radar

Transmit power, P_t	100 kW
Antenna gain, G	1,000
Mortar bomb RCS, σ	0.001 m^2
Radar wavelength, λ	0.03 m
Losses, L	20
Min detectable signal, S min	10^{-16} W
$R^4 = (P_t G^2 \sigma \lambda^2)/(64\pi^3 LS \text{ min})$	2.26×10^{16}
Max range, R	12.3 km

- The need to strike a balance between equipment size and all weather performance leads to a carrier frequency of about 10 GHz.
- The small size of the mortar bomb RCS demands both high pulse power, and high antenna gain which means a narrow bandwidth. The beam must then be scanned rapidly back and forth over the azimuth coverage sector at a rate sufficient to ensure detection of the bomb wherever it may appear within the sector.
- The fan shaped scan pattern should be as near the ground as possible to obtain an initial fix of the bomb early in its flight.
- As soon as the detection and fix have been made, the fan pattern must be moved to a higher elevation to locate the bomb at a point further along its path. This may be done by a rapid antenna displacement.
- The range R, the azimuth angle ϕ, and the elevation angle θ for each fan scan elevation is passed to the computer which determines the position of the mortar.
- Figure 6.4 shows the concept of the two fan scan elevation technique. Figure 1.3 also illustrates the action.
- It should be noted that this method is not suitable for the fix of several weapons at one time.
- Ground clutter rejection must be good so that a small resolution cell is essential, as noted in Chapter 3. The volume of a cell is given by:

$$V = (R^2 \theta \phi c\tau)/2.$$

A minimum volume is achieved by the use of a narrow antenna beam and wide bandwidth transmission (short pulse). The Doppler shift of a mortar bomb alone cannot be relied on to give adequate clutter discrimination.

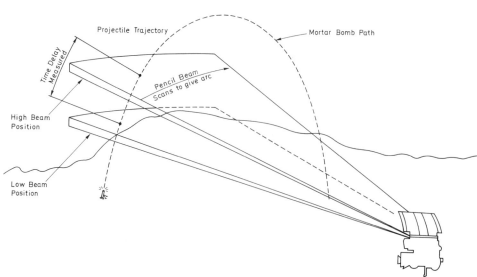

FIG. 6.4   Two fan scan technique

- The range performance of such a system will depend on the RCS of the mortar bomb. This is mainly produced by the tail fins of the round. The application of stealth techniques will reduce the performance of existing equipments and this must be considered in new designs. These radars may be mounted on many different types of vehicle but in every case it is essential that they should be capable of being brought into and out of action quickly without the need for a large crew. The need to conceal the presence of a WLR from the enemy leads to the requirement for a low visual, infra red (IR), and acoustic signature, which means the provision of a quiet generator.

Figure 6.5 shows the Thorn EMI *Cymbeline*, a widely deployed western WLR, while Figure 6.6 depicts a Soviet system known in the West as *Big Fred*. It is of interest that the antenna has a similar appearance in these two systems. The British system is advertised as using a Foster scanning antenna with a mechanical switch of the beam from low to high angle. It seems probable that the Soviet radar uses a similar technique, particularly as Soviet surface-to-air radars are known to use rotating cone scanners. The latest version of the *Cymbeline* employs an electronically scanned phased array antenna.

Recently Introduced Systems

In common with many other items of high technology military equipment, WLR have become so costly to develop and manufacture that they can be produced only by the superpowers or by international consortia of firms.

The generation of WLR now entering service in many countries, including Nato, may be represented by the *Fire Finder* system which the Hughes Company of the United States produces. It consists of two radar equipments, the AN/TPQ 36 (Figure 6.7) and the AN/TPQ 37 (Figure 6.8).

FIG. 6.5   *Cymbeline (Courtesy Thorn EMI Electronics Ltd)*

FIG. 6.6   *Big Fred (Crown Copyright/MOD photograph)*

FIG. 6.7 AN/TPQ 36 *(Courtesy Hughes Aircraft Company)*

The AN/TPQ 36, although primarily intended for mortar location, may also be used to locate rocket launchers and short range field guns. For this reason it uses not only range and angle discrimination, but Doppler gating as well. It was designed *ab initio* with a complex computer facility which, among other functions, allows the exclusion of false targets such as birds and aircraft by recognition of their characteristic trajectories. The antenna is a phased array system giving rapid beam positioning of a pencil beam, over an arc of 90° in azimuth. Figure 6.9 illustrates how a phased array may operate for the WLR need. Monopulse tracking of several targets can be undertaken while the search for new targets continues. The automatic computation and output provides map co-ordinates of the located weapons, including height correction, provided terrain data has been fed into the computer memory. High density of fire can be processed. Subsequent rounds from weapons already located can be rejected, thus permitting the system to concentrate on new data. The phased array antenna can be programmed to provide a sector sweep which matches the horizon profile, thus forming an alerting 'fence'. This fence detects the projectiles as early in their trajectory as possible. Output data from the system is available in digital form which can be passed directly to a compatible fire control computer. It has been reported that the WLR has on some occasions enabled counter battery fire to precede the impact of the original enemy projectile which gave weapon location. This system may be used to track departing counter battery rounds, thus acting as a gun correction radar (see Chapter 8). The vastly improved capability of this radar as compared with first generation systems

FIG. 6.8   AN/TPQ 37 *(Courtesy Hughes Aircraft Company)*

owes much to new developments in antenna design, improved coherent transmitter technology, and greatly enhanced computer power. The size, weight, generator requirement and cost have inevitably also increased, as has the signature on the battlefield.

The AN/TPQ 37 uses much of the same technology as the above system but is intended for the location of long range guns beyond the ability of the AN/TPQ 36. The two systems are therefore complementary. It is provided with a larger antenna of greater gain and a more powerful transmitter. This leads to a larger generator and a longer time into action.

The most difficult target of such a system is the head on shell, fired at low angle, close to the terrain, at long range from the radar. This makes heavy demands on both clutter rejection and power on target.

Near Future Outlook

The multinational consortium EURO-ART has announced its intention to develop a new WLR under the name *Cobra* (counter battery radar). An artist's

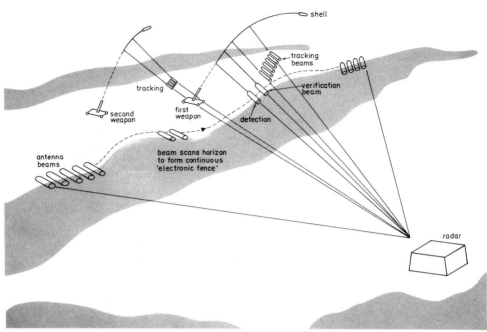

FIG. 6.9   Operation of phased array weapon locating radar

impression of this system is shown in Figure 6.10. It is in response to a trinational requirement (West Germany, France, UK) for a long range WLR optimised for counter battery operations. Detailed information of this requirement is not available for publication. However, modern battlefield conditions allow reasonable speculation as to the probable technical capability of this proposed system. It may be expected to have an extension of the characteristics of the AN/TPQ 37 with some improvements made possible by recent advances in antenna design, computer technology and new materials. Additional emphasis is likely to be placed on full automation with the ability of operator intervention if required. Increased mobility, reduced manpower, and reduced time into and out of action may be looked for. The growing importance of electronic warfare (EW) in the field will add to the desirability for reduced signature to diminish the effectiveness of enemy ESM and anti-radiation missile (ARM) operations. This LPI need will probably result in a wide bandwidth transmission system. The need to integrate all equipment into the modern data signal networks and communication systems must also be considered. A further desirable feature which might become available is the provision of an external alerting system which would allow visual, IR, acoustic, or some other source of alarm to enable radar silence to be maintained until the enemy guns or rocket launchers are actually brought into action.

There is always a temptation, when highly expensive military hardware is under development, to look for multipurpose capability or fall back roles which the system will be able to undertake. Such elaboration of the specification has in the past usually resulted in longer development time, and in many cases less effective performance of the primary role. In the case of a WLR it is most doubtful if it would be an advantage to call for secondary ability, such as helicopter detection.

FIG. 6.10   *Cobra* weapon locating radar *(Courtesy Thorn EMI Electronics Ltd)*

Possible Future Systems

The high cost and complexity of modern WLR raises the question which is now occurring in several aspects of defence equipment, namely the possibility of using modern technical advances to develop WLR of simple capability, which are small and relatively inexpensive. The requirement for such systems might well arise in armies not closely associated with those of the highly developed nations. Such a radar should be easy to operate without lengthy training, and should have high reliability. The range would be short. It is not unknown for simplified military equipment produced by private firms for an unsophisticated market to be subsequently adopted by major national forces.

7

Air Defence Radar

The Air Defence Task

The threat from the air-to-ground forces is considerable. Hostile aircraft can approach rapidly and with little warning, release their weapons, and depart, only to return later to renew their assault. Missiles pose a similar problem. Their approach is also rapid and can be from a wide range of elevations. Consequently, warning times are often minimal. Obviously the problem of air defence is one of the greatest priority, and ground forces would find a proper system of air defence greatly to their advantage.

The purpose of any system of air defence is to detect and destroy hostile airborne assets before they can do damage. Thus the key elements in the system are detection and destruction:

- *Detection*. The crucial issue in the detection of airborne threats is timeliness as early detection gives the defenders time to organise the destruction of the target. Since airborne targets tend to approach rapidly, this essentially means that detection should take place at the longest possible range. Radar is a sensor that performs well in this role, and thus it is not surprising that air defence systems use it for the early detection of threats. Radars used in this fashion are generally known as search, or surveillance, radars.
- *Destruction*. Once timely detection has taken place, the system will operate to destroy the threat. The method used will depend on detection range and scenario. Targets detected at long range can be intercepted by friendly aircraft and destroyed while still at long range. At shorter ranges, and in situations where no friendly interceptors are available, SAMs or anti-aircraft artillery (AAA) would be more appropriate. In order to guide an aircraft or missile onto its target, accurate and continuous measurement of target location is required. Similar data is required to aim AAA correctly. This measurement activity, known as tracking, is well suited to radar, and one finds its use in this part of the AD system also.

This chapter aims to outline the use of radar in the above roles, and to show how the differing operational requirements dictate differing radar designs. In practice those operational requirements are driven by the perceived threat and are extremely varied. However, for our purposes, the simplest approach is to classify AD radars in terms of the detection range required by the system. The range classifications are:

- *Strategic*. Strategic systems have a requirement for target detection at thousands of kilometres. At these ranges the threat is mainly from interconti- nental ballistic missiles (ICBMs) or from submarine launched ballistic missiles (SLBMs). However, the threat from orbital vehicles should not be discounted, and thus space surveillance is also undertaken by this type of radar.
- *Long range*. Long range systems have a requirement for target detection at ranges of 200 nm (370 km) upwards. The threat is usually from aircraft, but long range missiles should not be neglected.
- *Medium range*. Medium range systems have a requirement for target detection of around 100 nm (185 km). Again, the threat may be aircraft or missile.
- *Short range*. Short range systems have a requirement for target detection at ranges of 30 nm (55 km) downwards.

AD radars will be discussed in the above order.

Strategic Radars

Strategic systems are part of continental defence. ICBMs and SLBMs are typical targets. Ideally, the aim of a strategic system would be the detection and destruction of incoming ballistic missiles. In fact such anti-ballistic missile systems have been proposed. In practice, however, a ballistic missile is a very difficult target to destroy. Consequently these systems have tended to concentrate on giving maximum warning time of missile arrival and on the early prediction of missile impact points. As a result strategic systems are required to detect and track incoming threats at ranges of several thousand kilometres.

Surveillance

The requirement for detection at such long ranges, coupled with the small RCS of the target, forces the use of high average transmitter power and large antenna aperture. Also, atmospheric attenuation can be a serious problem at these ranges, and it is necessary to minimise it. This implies the use of a low transmitter frequency. All three of these requirements lead to a large and expensive system.

Tracking

In the past, surveillance and tracking were implemented by separate radar equipments. Nowadays, however, the development of multifunction phased array radars has allowed both activities to be undertaken by a single equipment. Given the large size and cost of these radars, this is obviously desirable.

Since there may well be many missiles incoming simultaneously, there is obviously a requirement for multiple target tracking. Also, since the purpose of tracking is to calculate impact points, a large processing capability is required.

Pave Paws, shown in Figure 7.1, is a modern example of such a radar. The transmitter frequency is in the low UHF band (420–450 MHz). High transmitter power is implemented by the use of a large number of distributed transmitter modules feeding two phased array antennas. The orientations of the two antennas differ by 120°, and each provides 120° of contiguous azimuth coverage, giving a

FIG. 7.1   *Pave Paws* phased array radar *(Courtesy Raytheon)*

total of 240° in all. Each antenna is fed by 1,792 transmitter modules, allowing the radar to produce an average power of up to 175 kW from each face.

Each array is roughly 30 m in diameter, giving the required large aperture. The resulting large building contains the sophisticated processing equipment required for multi-target tracking, and for the prediction of ballistic missile impact points and times. Originally designed for the protection of continental America against SLBMs, *Pave Paws* is also capable of detecting ICBMs and of space surveillance. The system is now being incorporated into the ballistic missile early warning system (BMEWS), with a site in Greenland recently commissioned, and work on a three-face radar, with 360° of coverage but otherwise working on the same principles, is progressing in the United Kingdom.

Long Range Radars

Long range radars are normally part of national, or large area, defence. Their primary function is the detection of incoming enemy aircraft early enough to allow interception and destruction by one's own AD aircraft well outside the area being defended. For example, assuming that it takes five minutes, say, from detection of the incoming threat to the take-off of the interceptor, and that both aircraft operate at Mach 2 (approximately 600 m/s), it can be shown that, if interception is to take place 100 km outside the defended area, detection must take place at a minimum range of 380 km (over 200 nm). Naturally, greater detection ranges give a more comfortable margin.

Surveillance

The requirement for long range detection forces the surveillance radar design to low transmission frequency, typically 1.3–3.0 GHz, and to high average power and large antenna aperture. Since these long range radars have necessarily to use a low PRF to avoid range ambiguity, they also have to use a low scan rate to allow a reasonable number of hits per scan. Since aircraft tend to try to avoid radar detection by flying low, good clutter suppression techniques are required. Nowadays these radars are also required to measure target elevation in addition to range and bearing, that is, they are 3D radars, and also to be transportable to enhance their survivability.

The *Martello* long range AD radar shown in Figure 7.2 is a good example of such a radar. Atmospheric attenuation is kept low by use of a transmission frequency of

FIG. 7.2   *Martello* transportable long range air defence radar *(Courtesy Marconi Radar Systems Ltd)*

about 1.3 GHz. An average output power of around 5 kW is achieved by the use of 40 transmitter/receiver modules, each of which feeds one horizontal row of the planar array antenna. The requirement for transportability limits the antenna size but it is still large enough to give a detection range of over 500 km (270 nm). This detection range implies a PRF of a few hundred hertz, and since the specified scan rate is 6 rpm through 360° of azimuth, the number of hits per scan is in the region of

10. The system uses mechanical scanning in azimuth and hence is not a fully phased array. However, the presence of distributed receivers, one per horizontal row of the planar array, allows the radar to use a signal processing technique known as post-detection beamforming to form a set of vertically stacked receive beams. Such an arrangement is often known as a stacked beam array; it is illustrated in Figure 7.3. This allows the system to measure elevation, and the

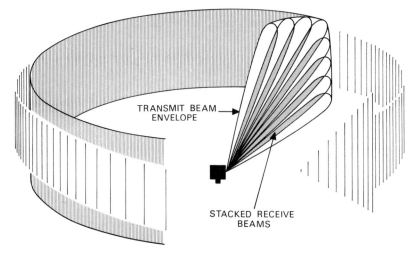

FIG. 7.3   Stacked beam array with mechanical azimuth scan

accuracy of this measurement is enhanced by the use of amplitude comparison monopulse techniques. The stacked beam arrangement also helps clutter rejection for all but the lowest flying targets. These are detected against the clutter background using MTI processing.

The ability to detect at long range using a ground based radar is clearly limited to high flying targets. This is because ground based sensors are limited by line of sight over the horizon, as shown in Figure 7.4. The relationship between line of

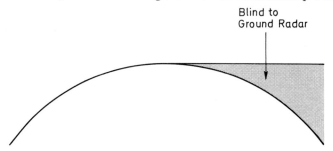

FIG. 7.4   Line of sight range limitation of a ground based radar

sight range R in nautical miles and target height h in feet is given by:

$$R = 1.23\sqrt{h}$$

From this it can be seen that detection at 200 nm (370 km) involves a target height of around 27,000 ft. Thus these radars are satisfactory against high flying targets, but become horizon limited against low fliers. The solution is to put the long range radar in the air, to produce an airborne early warning (AEW) radar. Flying the radar at a significant height above the ground increases the distance to the horizon, and thus increases the line of sight range of the system. The equation given above for line of sight range from a ground based radar to an airborne target works equally well for an airborne radar looking down on low flying targets. It can be seen that an AEW aircraft flying at 27,000 ft will be able to see all targets out to the horizon limitation of around 200 nm regardless of their altitude. In addition, against high flying targets, line of sight ranges are considerably enhanced. Both these situations are illustrated in Figure 7.5.

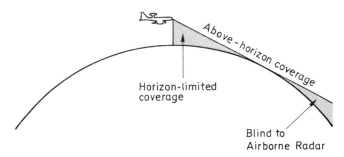

FIG. 7.5   Coverage of an airborne radar system

Taking a long range search radar into the air has two major implications:

- The radar is limited in size and weight by the airframe capacity. This has one of two effects:
  1. The radar must accept the degraded angle resolution caused by the increased beamwidth of the smaller antenna. A good example of this approach is found in the E2C *Hawkeye* aircraft, as the AEW system that it carries operates in the UHF band.
  2. The transmission frequency must be raised to compensate for the smaller antenna size. This is the approach used in AEWs such as the E3A *Sentinel*, of which more below.

- Since this radar is now operating in a look down mode, clutter becomes a problem against the majority of targets. Also, because the platform is moving, the standard ground based clutter rejection technique of MTI using delay lines is inadequate. Hence AEW radars are required to be pulse Doppler systems operating in high or medium PRF mode. Such radars are able to reject much of the ground clutter by the use of direct frequency discrimination, as described in Chapter 3. However, the use of a high PRF mode involves the presence of range ambiguities, while medium PRF involves the presence of ambiguities in both range and velocity. These can be resolved by using multiple PRF transmissions coupled with appropriate receiver processing. It should be noted that the use of an antenna with very low sidelobes is also a necessity.

The airborne warning and control system (AWACS), carried by the *Sentinel*

(E3A) aircraft, is illustrated in Figure 7.6, and is currently perhaps the most sophisticated fielded AEW. The radar operates at 3 GHz; any higher frequency would run into unacceptable attenuation. The use of a high precision slotted waveguide array antenna, designed in conjunction with its rotodome, has produced the excellent sidelobe performance of approximately −60 dB. When flown at 30,000 ft, the system would have a range to the horizon of roughly 215 nm. When looking for targets against the clutter background, the system operates in the high PRF regime, and employs suitable processing to resolve the range ambiguities inherent in this mode of transmission. When looking for targets above the horizon, clutter is no longer a problem. This allows the system to operate in a low PRF mode and hence removes the need for the resolution of range ambiguities. The system is designed for the detection of both aircraft and missiles.

Tracking

The tracking requirement associated with long range systems is primarily that involved in guiding the interceptor onto its target. This has two main aspects, discussed below.

Ground Controlled Intercept

The user of the surveillance radar designates the target to the radar. The radar then outputs target range, bearing and altitude every scan, and these parameters are used to guide the interceptor towards its intercept point. This procedure is known as Ground Controlled Intercept (GCI), and can be considered here as part of the tracking side of the AD system. The same process can also be achieved from an AEW aircraft; the technique is the same, but the name is clearly rather less appropriate.

Airborne Intercept

Once the interceptor has its target within the detection range of its own radar, it can lock on, and then close to intercept autonomously. If the interceptor is to do this effectively, its radar must be quite sophisticated. First, it must be able to operate in search, acquisition, and tracking modes, that is to say it must be a multi-mode radar. Second, it should ideally have an all aspect look down capability, and the best possible detection capability in the forward hemisphere. This involves the use of a modern pulse Doppler radar to overcome the clutter problem. All aspect capability is best obtained with the use of a medium PRF system; maximum capability in the forward hemisphere is best obtained using high PRF. The modern solution is to interleave high and medium PRFs on a scan by scan basis. Third, it should have a track-while-scan capability. This allows the interceptor to monitor a number of targets simultaneously, which in turn allows multiple engagements to take place.

The design of a radar conforming to the above requirements is clearly a demanding task. It is made even more difficult by the space, weight and power limitations imposed by the aircraft that carries it. However, a number of very

FIG. 7.6   *Sentinel* aircraft showing AWACS antenna and rotodome assembly *(Courtesy Westinghouse Defense International)*

successful designs do exist around the world. A British example of such a radar is the *Blue Vixen*, produced by GEC Ferranti Defence Systems Ltd for the *Sea Harrier* aircraft. The radar is shown in Figure 7.7. The unit at the top left of the picture contains the flat plate antenna (covered here for reasons of security), the transmitter, and the receiver. This whole unit is naturally located in the aircraft nose. The other two white boxes are (left) the transmitter auxiliary power supply and (right) the signal and data processor. The two black boxes are the cockpit display and its control display interface. The entire package is achieved with an all up weight of under 150 kg. It has recently been announced that the same British company will be providing the radar for the European Fighter Aircraft. This is expected to be of even more modern design, and to have a significantly greater capability than pulse Doppler radars currently fielded.

Medium Range Radars

Medium range air defence radars normally form part of a missile tactical area defence system. The required detection range for this kind of system depends very much on the range capability of the associated missile system, but is typically of the order of 100 nm (185 km). This order of detection range would allow the system to be used to cue interceptors if they were being held on combat air patrol (CAP). However, this represents a rather specialist use of the system's capability, and discussion in this chapter will be confined to the use of medium range radars in conjunction with SAM systems.

The tactical requirement placed on medium range systems requires them to be

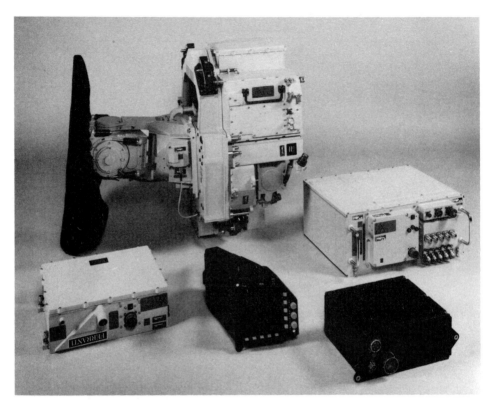

FIG. 7.7   *Blue Vixen* radar *(Courtesy GEC Ferranti Defence Systems Ltd)*

mobile. This, added to the fact that the required area of coverage is obviously much smaller, makes it more common to find surveillance and tracking radars co-located, or even as different operating modes of the same radar. It is also the normal situation to have the radar system in the same location as the missile system it is serving.

In this discussion the surveillance and tracking functions have been treated separately, to ease their description. However, the whole AD system is in fact a single entity, and it must not be forgotten that the design of any part of the radar system will be affected by the required performance of the AD system as a whole. This will become obvious in the discussion which follows.

Surveillance

In the long range systems described above, the required detection range of the surveillance radar was dictated by the requirement to achieve timely intercept. The situation is very much the same in medium range systems. The 'interceptor' in this case is the missile, and timely intercept involves the destruction of the target at maximum missile range. The required detection range of the radar in its surveillance mode is therefore determined by the maximum range of the missile. However, since the target is moving, allowance must be made for:

- The distance it can travel between detection and missile launch,
- How far it can travel during the missile flight time.

Taking the second point first, if it is assumed that both target and missile travel at the same velocity, missile launch should take place at about the moment the target is at distance equal to twice the missile maximum range. An example will illustrate this. Suppose that the missile has a maximum range of 60 km. In the time that it flies out to this distance, the target travelling at the same speed has also flown 60 km. It follows that, if the missile is to meet the target at a range of 60 km, the target must have been 120 km distant at the moment of missile launch, and this is twice the missile range. This reasoning applies for any missile range one might choose.

Now let us examine the first point. The system will take time to go from initial detection to missile launch, as it goes through the following stages:

- In order to avoid the problem of false alarms, the surveillance radar confirms detection by looking for the target on a number of consecutive scans, typically three. If the target is positively detected on each scan, the detection is confirmed and the target parameters are used to acquire and track the target.
- The target parameters provided by the surveillance radar is not in general accurate enough for the tracker. The surveillance radar is usually of lower transmitter frequency than the tracker. If they are using the same antenna, the surveillance beamwidth is necessarily the greater. If different antennas are used, the surveillance radar is not necessarily measuring altitude at all, and even if it is, may be operating with a fan beam which does not give great elevation accuracy. Therefore the radar refines the target parameters for the tracker by using a narrow pencil beam to perform a limited raster scan in the region of the target. This process is known as target acquisition.
- Once a more accurate measurement of target location is available, the tracker can lock on to the target and start supplying the data required for the missile. In practical systems the acquisition process is frequently carried out by the tracker itself rather than by a separate acquisition radar. It does, after all, have the required narrow pencil beam.

The time taken to perform the stages outlined above depends on the surveillance scan rate, the accuracy of the surveillance target parameters, and the speed of the acquisition process. All these tend to depend on the range of the system but in practice 30 s in total would not be far wrong.

From the discussion in the above paragraphs it is clear that initial detection must take place while the target range is still substantially more than twice the missile range. A good rule of thumb is to require detection at roughly three times the range of the missile. This is known as three to one gearing.

It should be noted that, although medium range AD systems have been defined as those requiring detection ranges of around 100 nm (185 km), it would be more realistic to define such systems as those with missile ranges in the very broad area of 30 nm (60 km), as it is the missile capability that drives the rest of the design.

Since the required detection range of the surveillance radar is smaller than that needed by a long range system, its design will differ from long range counterpart in a number of ways:

- Average transmitter power can be lower. This reduces the demands on the power supply, allowing it to be smaller. This helps in the design of a mobile system.
- Antenna aperture can be reduced, allowing a physically smaller antenna. Since the antenna size makes up a significant portion of the volume of the radar equipment, this allows the design of a smaller mobile radar.
- Transmitter frequency can be raised because atmospheric attenuation is less of a problem. This allows the retention of high antenna gain on transmission despite the smaller antenna aperture. It also tends to produce smaller components within the radar, once again aiding system mobility.
- The reduced detection range allows a reduction in maximum unambiguous range, hence the radar can operate with a higher PRF. This allows a higher scan rate to be implemented and shortens the detection process.

A combination of these considerations produces a surveillance radar which operates at around 5 GHz and, depending on precise detection range requirements, a PRF of 800–2,000 Hz, a scan rate of 12–30 rpm, and an antenna diameter of 3 m down to 1 m, respectively.

Tracking

In the long range systems discussed earlier, the final tracking function is carried out by the interceptor once it has acquired its target. This is essentially an autonomous process as the interceptor has its own radar. It is also a necessary process as tracking information derived from a radar 100 km away from the intercept will not be accurate enough to guide the interceptor's weapon onto the target. In principle, this final tracking could be done with an active homing head within a long range missile, removing the need for the interceptor altogether. However, it tends to be very expensive as the whole missile and all its contents are used only once. Therefore, although such an approach is used against high value assets in anti-ship missiles, it is not appropriate in air defence.

The presence of the pilot has another advantage in that he can visually identify the target prior to attack. This is still the most reliable form of IFF.

In the medium range systems being discussed here, there is no interceptor. Therefore the guidance of the missile onto its target must be carried out either by the radar system or by the missile itself, or by a combination of the two. Four possible strategies present themselves and are listed below. Please note, however, that they are only outlined here, as detailed discussion of missile guidance systems is outside the scope of this book. More detail on this subject can be obtained from the companion Volume 1 *Guided Weapons*.

Active Homing Guidance

The missile has an active tracking radar in its homing head. The surveillance radar provides target parameters to the missile so that its tracking radar can lock on, then missile launch takes place. In practice this option is inappropriate because the transmitter power needed for detection out to at least twice missile range is too high to be implemented in a missile which is required to be mostly motor and warhead. Also, as mentioned, active homing systems are very expensive.

Command Guidance

A radar on the ground monitors the target location continuously and guides the missile to its target via guidance commands down a communication link. This obviates the need for any radar at all in the missile. The accuracy of the tracking radar falls off inversely with range, and this method is therefore more satisfactory at shorter ranges than it is at longer ranges. Given that a tracking radar can track in angle to a typical accuracy of 0.01 of a beamwidth, one could expect this method to give an accuracy of 20 m or so at 60 km using a 2° beam.

Semi-Active Homing Guidance

A tracking radar on the ground illuminates the target with high power, giving a strong target echo which is detected by a suitable tracker in the missile, and used for homing. The ground based tracker only needs to be accurate enough to get illumination on to the target. Homing accuracy is provided by the tracker in the missile, and this gets more accurate as it closes on the target. Also, since the radar in the missile is receive only, its power requirements are very small with the consequent reduction in weight, size and cost.

Track via Missile Guidance

A combination of command guidance and semi-active guidance can be used. Sometimes bearing the alternative name of ground aided seeker, in its normal implementation, this is a complex form of semi-active homing in which the tracking information obtained by the missile seeker head is transmitted to the ground, where the guidance computations are performed. At the same time the equipment on the ground generates its own tracking information by monitoring both target and missile. The guidance computations are thus the result of two different sets of tracking data. The resulting guidance commands, which are in general more accurate than would be obtained from a single set of data, are transmitted back to the missile. This approach is costly but is very flexible. In particular, in the face of enemy ECM, the system has the ability to revert to autonomous semi-active homing or to autonomous command guidance. This makes the system very resistant to jamming.

If active homing guidance is excluded, all the remaining options involve the use of a tracking radar that is not carried by the missile. Therefore the radar system must include such a radar, either as a separate equipment or as an operating mode of the surveillance radar. In practice the size and weight advantages of using a common antenna for both roles are impressive. There is much to be gained, therefore, in designing a single equipment which can carry out both the surveillance and the tracking roles. However there are difficulties to be overcome in this approach. Once a conventional radar system starts tracking, its antenna will be staring at the target. It follows that it is no longer carrying out its surveillance function as this involves scanning the rest of the required coverage area. This limits the capability of the system to a single target. In the past, radar design could not overcome this obstacle and systems were either designed with single target capability only, that is with surveillance ceasing as soon as tracking starts, or with separate, multiple trackers to allow multiple engagement capability. While the former approach may well be very effective in short range point defence systems, discussed below, the latter approach is very desirable in medium range area defence systems.

The modern solution to this problem lies in the development of phased array radars. These radars, which use electronic scanning techniques, can time-share the two roles, switching between functions a number of times each second. The speed of the switching is such that both surveillance and tracking are effectively continuous, and thus the system has true multiple target capability both in surveillance and tracking.

A modern example of a medium range tactical air defence system is the American *Patriot*, which is illustrated in Figure 7.8. *Patriot* uses a space fed phased array of just under 2.5 m diameter, as shown in Figure 7.9. It gives the radar the

FIG. 7.8 Deployment of the *Patriot* air defence radar system *(Courtesy Raytheon)*

capability for simultaneous surveillance and multiple target tracking. The system is mobile and operates a missile with a range of around 60 km. The missile employs track via missile guidance. As noted, it is costly but flexible and, in particular, very resistant to ECM.

FIG. 7.9   *Patriot* phased array antenna *(Courtesy Raytheon)*

Identification, Friend or Foe

This section would be incomplete without some reference to IFF using secondary surveillance radar (SSR). This facility is automatic and has the object of alerting the defensive side that its target is friendly, thus preventing engagement. The basic principle is as follows. The transmitted signal from the main radar is received by a special receiver on board a friendly aircraft. It triggers a response which is received by the surveillance radar on the ground. The response from the aircraft contains the necessary information to identify it as friendly to the defences. In the absence of a suitable response, any detected target is treated as hostile. Although simple in principle, the technique has some practical drawbacks in that any friendly aircraft whose IFF equipment is inoperative is treated as hostile. The same applies to neutral and to civilian forces. The system also has to be sophisticated enough to prevent genuinely hostile forces from imitating the correct response and thus obtaining immunity from attack. Visual identification does not have these drawbacks but it is rather limited in range. As an IFF technique, therefore, it does not compete effectively with SSR in the majority of situations, and is mainly used to give final confirmation of the hostile nature of the target whenever this is possible. An example of this procedure in action is given in the section on long range radars, where SSR is used to eliminate targets with friendly responses. However, visual identification of apparently hostile targets by the interceptor is still desirable prior to weapon release.

Some form of IFF is clearly a vital part of any system of air defence. For the medium range systems discussed here, given their required detection range of about 100 nm, SSR is the most viable, indeed probably the only, option. In the short range systems outlined below, it might be possible to use visual identification for IFF but in practice, where initial detection is made by a surveillance radar, SSR is still a great advantage.

Short Range Radars

Short range systems have a detection range requirement of less than 30 nm (55 km). Using the three to one gearing mentioned above, one would expect them to be used in conjunction with a missile of range less than 10 nm (18 km). Such logic leads one to the conclusion that the purpose of a short range air defence system is point defence, as missile ranges of this order will not be very effective as area defence weapons. Point defence systems are intended to give last ditch protection to the specific installation to which they are assigned. As such they are inevitably short range, and intended to deal with air threats that the long and medium range systems have failed to detect and destroy. They are required to be very quick in their reaction, and the requirement for good and instant IFF is obvious. Also, one would expect them to be very mobile.

Many systems of this type will not use radar surveillance at all, but will rely on visual and IR detection instead. However, visual systems do not have the capability to operate effectively at night, and IR systems are not all weather. It follows, therefore, that there is still a need for radar surveillance, if it can be afforded. Where a short range system uses radar surveillance and radar tracking, it is to be expected that the equipments will be co-located, and very probably different operating modes of a single equipment. However, as in the previous section, the two will be treated separately for purposes of clarity.

Surveillance

The effect of a much reduced range requirement as compared with medium range systems leads to a number of changes in the design of the surveillance radar:

- The required transmitter power is greatly reduced, making power supply requirements much lower. Radars of this type have a typical average power requirement of under 100 W.
- Atmospheric attenuation becomes far less important, allowing much higher transmitter frequencies, even up to the millimetric bands. Consequently much smaller components are possible.
- A smaller antenna can be used without the loss of gain on transmission.

- The PRF and scan rate can be raised significantly, allowing much more rapid detection and acquisition.

Tracking

The much reduced range also has implications for the approach to target tracking and missile guidance:

- Command Guidance becomes more favourable as an option as linear errors decrease with range. In situations where it is accurate enough this is an attractive approach. At these short ranges, command guidance is fairly resistant to jamming as all the anti-jam capability is concentrated into the ground equipment. Active homing also becomes more feasible from the point of view of required transmitter power. It is still an expensive option, however, as all guidance and anti-jam capability is carried in the missile and is used only once. In practice active homing is almost unknown in this type of system.
- Since warning times and engagement times are so short, it is very probable that the system needs only deal with one target at a time. This means that a design in which surveillance and tracking are two modes of the same radar is much more viable. Thus the expensive option of a phased array is less necessary and it is common to find the more conventional approach, in which the surveillance mode lapses at the beginning of the tracking phase to be re-established only at the end of the engagement.
- The shorter missile range, coupled with the greater guidance accuracy mentioned above, allows the design of a missile with a smaller warhead, and lower fuel and motor requirements. This implies an altogether smaller weapon so that it is practicable to carry both radar system and missiles on the same small vehicle.

An example of a short range point defence system that has had much success over many years is the British system *Rapier*. The system originally consisted of a search and acquisition radar housed under a radome and carried on the same trailer as four missiles. They were required to hit the target to achieve a kill. The whole was towed by a long wheelbase Land Rover. The assembly is shown in Figure 7.10. The system originally used the surveillance radar with a continuous 360° scan pattern to detect incoming threats on any bearing and to measure threat direction. The information provided was used to alert the operator and to give him the direction in which to look. He then took control of missile release and used an optical sight to command guide the missile to its target. The success of the system has ensured a long in-service life, and this has allowed a number of improvements in the original specification:

- A dedicated tracked vehicle has been produced as an alternative to the original trailer configuration. It is known as *Tracked Rapier*.
- As described above, the original tracking system was optical in nature. The development of the *Blindfire* tracking radar has now produced an alternative tracking system which can operate in both day and night. *Blindfire* is a millimetric monopulse tracking radar that can track both target and missile. It

FIG. 7.10   *Rapier* short range air defence system *(Courtesy British Aerospace)*

enables the use of a differential tracking technique in which the radar monitors the missile's angular error from line of sight to the target. The guidance is still command guidance but now the process can be made automatic.

- Currently, the missile requires actually to hit the target to detonate the warhead. Such missiles, commonly known as hittiles, have the advantage of not requiring proximity fuzes. However, on-missile electronics is becoming cheaper and lighter all the time and therefore it is proposed to fit the system with a proximity fuze at some time in the future. This will relax the tracking and guidance requirements.

Rapier is a good example of the design points that have been made above. It operates off a single platform, is highly mobile, has rapid response, and engages one target at a time. It does use two different radars but this is the consequence of the *Blindfire* option arriving as an 'add-on' after initial fielding of the equipment.

Summary

The detail of this chapter has produced a number of broad themes which are summarised here:

- The design of the radar system within an AD system is driven by the operational requirement. In particular, the detection range of the surveillance radar is driven by the required range of target intercept and destruction.
- As the area to be protected becomes smaller, so the tracking and guidance aspects of the radar system become steadily more important because they become more and more the province of the ground equipment rather than that of the interceptor or SAM.

- As the range of the system comes down, response times also reduce with the consequence that reliable IFF becomes ever more vital.
- As the range of the system comes down, radar frequencies, PRFs and scan rates increase, transmission powers and equipment sizes decrease, and systems become ever more mobile.

8

Other Battlefield Radars

Possibilities

The main uses of radar on the battlefield have been the subject of other chapters. However, there are one or two other roles played by radar, which have had their place in modern armies for some years. These will now be covered briefly as they are of relatively small combat importance at the present time, although it may well be that some will assume greater importance in the future.

Modern developments in radar technology, particularly the extension of radar into the millimetre wavelength (MMW) region, and the recent explosive advance in the power of signal processing in both the electronic and the optical (that is, the use of light to carry signals) area, now provide the spur to the trial of new battlefield radar systems. Some likely new uses will be discussed but it is too early to say which of these new equipments will prove of sufficient value to appear in the ever more costly array of battlefield hardware.

Velocity Measurement of Projectiles

The use of radar on trials ranges for the testing of weapon systems is an essential element of trials instrumentation, but this lies outside the subject of this book. However, radars similar to some used for this purpose find a role in the operation of artillery. Field guns rely greatly on the observation of the fall of shot to provide data for aim correction. This involves the location of the mean point of impact of a random scatter of rounds onto the chosen target. One of the main variables producing this scatter is round to round variation of muzzle velocity. A small radar situated at the gun position can measure the initial velocity of successive shells by the determination of Doppler shift. From the results, the required adjustment can be computed with fewer samples of observed fire.

The shell, observed from the rear, provides a small circular cross section, which precludes the use of CP. However, the range is short, and the range rate is high giving good Doppler discrimination. The direction of the antenna can be preset and fixed, relative to the gun barrel. Such a requirement suggests a low power continuous wave (CW) radar using a simple antenna such as circular dish or lens with circulator duplexing. The need to observe departing shells having maximum specified angular launch dispersion dictates the beam width and hence the gain of the antenna for a given size and frequency. The magnitude of this beamwidth will depend greatly on the type of weapon, but might be of the order of 8°. The carrier frequency can be high, as atmospheric attenuation is unlikely to be a problem at the short ranges needed. The system should be low cost and very rugged to survive the severe environment, close to the gun. Battery power should suffice to provide the short periods of use. The Doppler shift of the returned signal relative to the transmitted frequency is given by $f = 2v/\lambda$ where v is the muzzle velocity of the shell and λ is the radar carrier wavelength. Thus for a velocity of 2,000 m/s and a wavelength of 2 mm, the Doppler shift would be 1 MHz.

It is most likely that there will be a future requirement, in the field, to track outgoing projectiles or missiles with high precision. In such a case the development of a radar such as that shown in Figure 8.1 may be expected. This

FIG. 8.1   Weibel radar tracker *(Courtesy Weibel Equipment Inc)*

highly accurate instrument is currently used for trials. Range data can be obtained by Doppler integration from a known start point. Angle information is derived from phase comparison monopulse using the phased array antenna.

Balloon Tracking Radar

Determination on the battlefield of meteorological conditions, and in particular wind profiles, may be required for several reasons including fall of shot correction and the launch of small unmanned aircraft (UMA). This may be achieved by releasing a small hydrogen balloon carrying a RCS enhancer such as a corner reflector. If this is tracked by a ground based radar, the physical path of the balloon can be made available to a computer which can then determine the local wind profile. It is unusual for there to be a need for long range tracking of the balloon but if there is, a transponder can be carried instead of a corner reflector. A radio sonde, capable of sending data on such parameters as temperature and barometric pressure, may also be carried but this would normally work independently of the radar.

A radar suitable for this activity, the block diagram of which is given in Figure 8.2, should provide good angular and range accuracy, but it would not have to work against much clutter or target noise. A simple conical scan tracker using a parabolic dish antenna and short pulse non-coherent transmission should suffice. The antenna servos would have a performance related to the maximum wind speeds expected. An example of such a radar is shown in Figure 8.3.

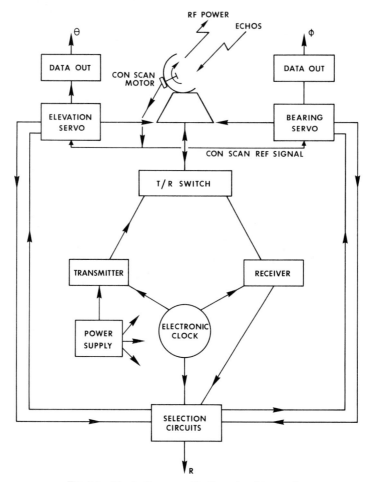

FIG. 8.2   Block diagram of balloon tracking radar

The short pulse would also allow the balloon to be tracked when it was released near the radar, as the T/R duplexer would quickly revert to the received state. The main production of such radars is for civilian use so that the military equivalent is normally of the same design, perhaps with some degree of modification for field use.

FIG. 8.3   Balloon tracking radar *(Courtesy CIT)*

Free Flight Rocket Correction Radar

The use of BSRs to correct fall of shot has been discussed in Chapter 5. In this situation the usual method is to locate the position of ground burst by line of sight observation of the target area by the BSR.

A variation of this method may be used when the target lies 'over the hill'. A narrow beam tracking radar is directed so that it can observe the last section of the missile trajectory before it disappears below the horizon. The first round fired consists of a special air burst radar shell or rocket which produces a chaff cloud, small in spatial spread but large RCS. The location of this burst by the radar allows the computer to remove gross bias error relative to the known ground position of the target. The launcher or gun direction can then be adjusted.

It is unlikely that the demand for this type of radar would justify the expense of a totally new design. A modified design of simple tracking radar may be expected. One similar to the balloon tracker might be used, but a longer pulse could be accepted as the radar target range is long and angular precision is of greater importance than that of range.

Unmanned Aircraft Radar

The recent rapid development in small pilotless aircraft, in infra red sensors, and in optical fibre transmission of wide bandwidth data has generated an interest in the possible production of small unmanned reconnaissance vehicles (UMRV) which might or might not be one mission expendable.

Such a system might well include a small low power radar for poor weather observation, when optical or IR sensors would be unsatisfactory. The concept of synthetic aperture surveillance has been described in Chapter 3. For this role the range of the sensor would be small from a low altitude UMA. Atmospheric attenuation would therefore be limited, permitting the use of MMW radar. The small wavelength and wide available transmission bandwidth would give good resolution both along track and cross track but the accuracy of the motion compensation and other processing required would need to be improved. The copious information obtained in real time by this radar would need a wide bandwidth transmission path back to its ground base. For a low flying UMA, the line of sight from the ground base to the radar would become obscured soon after launch so that, in order to avoid a costly airborne relay platform, the use of an optical fibre, unspooled by the UMA, would provide an attractive alternative. Figure 8.4 illustrates the concept. The wide transmission bandwidth made available by the use of the optical fibre permits the high data rate needed to pass the information obtained by the radar. It is also not susceptible to jamming.

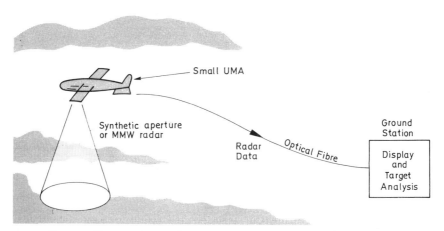

FIG. 8.4   Unmanned aircraft with radar sensor and optical fibre data link

Systems of the type outlined above have yet to be developed to the point where they can enter field service. There are several areas of technical risk, not only in the design of MMW antennas, signal processing, and transmitters, but also in the engineering of a suitable aircraft, giving a stable platform for the radar, and possessing adequate performance and navigation capability.

The problem of dispensing the optical fibre has been the subject of practical tests with guided weapons, and ranges of 20 km or more are considered feasible, depending on the size of the UMA. It is possible to achieve a smaller size, in the case of a reusable UMA, by reducing its return phase payload. If, for example, its purpose is reconnaisance, it can fly back with a silent radar. The fibre can be discarded while the UMA flies back under navigation control. Thus the length of the fibre carried need be sufficient only for the outward flight.

Remotely Piloted Vehicle Tracking Radar

One sub-type of unmanned aircraft is the remotely piloted vehicle (RPV). This is a UMA which is flown by a remote control link. The pilot, or remote control operator, is situated on the ground or in a command aircraft. In some such systems, but not all, depending on the type of navigation used, it is necessary to track the air vehicle from the control station. A line of sight tracking radar rather than optical systems will be employed to do this in all but the very short range systems. The tracking function of the radar would be similar to those already discussed but as the radar target is part of the system, secondary radar using a transponder on the RPV will be chosen in most cases.

It is also highly likely that the command signals sent to the RPV will be provided by modulating the radar transmitter waveform with the required information. This technique has been incorporated in command guided missiles for many years. Several methods are possible but pulse position modulation is usually favoured, mainly because it does not require amplitude variation of the radar transmitter and the radar energy on target is maintained constant for all states of the information modulation.

Radar Anti-Tank Homing Missiles and Projectiles

Unlike the use of MMW radar for UMRV, which is in the early stages of consideration, and of uncertain future, the development of MMW radar homing missiles, mainly for the attack of the main battle tanks (MBT), has been the scene of intense and heavily funded activity since the mid 1980s. Figure 8.5 shows the multiple launch rocket system (MLRS) which in its phase I form is in service providing unguided rocket fire power. The phase III system, still under development, will use the unguided rocket as a carrier or bus vehicle which will deploy a number of guided sub-munitions, each fitted with a fully active homing eye. These will be specially designed to single out and attack armoured vehicles among other objects on the battlefield.

Figure 8.6 shows another approach, the *Merlin* mortar launched system, which could provide the standard 81 mm mortar with an ability to attack MBT with radar homing projectiles, if it were required.

Other systems under development will provide special rounds giving normal 155 mm field guns the ability to launch radar homing projectiles at approximately the usual range of the gun.

Further details of the above systems will not be given here (refer instead to Volume 4 on Ammunition) but the following section will discuss the important

FIG. 8.5   Multiple launch rocket system *(Courtesy Thorn EMI Electronics)*

FIG. 8.6   Guided mortar bomb *(Courtesy British Aerospace)*

factors which must be considered in the design of MMW homing heads for terminally guided munitions (TGM).

The MMW Radar Homing Head

The function of the homing head in guided weapons is to establish and continuously maintain a measurement of the direction of the target as seen from the missile. The rate of turn of this direction in inertial space, which is known as sight line spin, can be determined by rate gyroscopes or other instrumentation. The rate of turn of flight path, which will result in impact with the target, may then be derived. The principle of proportional navigation (PN) as used by most homing missiles is covered in Volume 1 on Guided Weapons. The essential radar element of the homing eye is a tracker observing the target from the missile. Although research is in progress to achieve this by means of electronic scanning of a fixed antenna array within or on the surface of the missile airframe, present systems, and those likely to be available in the near future, use a two plane gimballed antenna which swings inside the missile to keep its boresight on the target. The radar energy must pass out and return through the front cap, or radome, which gives the nose of the missile its correct aerodynamic shape, modified to minimise distortion of the radar waves. The radome must also be able to withstand possible launch shocks, aerodynamic heating, and the impact of rain or hail. The design of its material and shape is far from trivial. Most MMW radar under development use the 94 GHz ($\lambda = 3.19$ mm) spectral window in the atmosphere, and this will be assumed here. The antenna must be able to turn within the missile airframe over an arc big enough to give the maximum expected lookout angle, that is the angle between the target direction and the missile axis. The magnitude of this angle will depend on the details of the system but could be $35°$ or more.

Conical scan tracking, described in Chapter 3, was used on the first trial models, but systems entering service will almost certainly use monopulse angle error signal processing. A lightweight disc antenna carrying the monopulse feeds might prove suitable. This would pose small demands on the servo motors needed to move the antenna. However, as indicated below, polarisation diversity may be required so that there is scope for a number of new concepts in antenna design, particularly in those systems using a guided projectile with high acceleration launched from a gun.

Some simplified quantitative arguments will now be used to derive the order of magnitude of some of the important parameters of a typical system. Taking as a typical value for the effective aperture of the antenna a disc of 100 mm diameter, somewhat smaller than the airframe diameter, the beamwidth will be given by approximately:

$$\theta = \lambda/D = 3.19/100 \text{ mrad} = 32 \text{ mrad} = 1.83°.$$

The size of a MBT may be taken for the purpose of illustration as 3 m wide by 3 m high by 8 m long. The 32 mrad beam will be about 3 m across at 100 m. At ranges greater than this the radar beam will illuminate clutter surrounding the tank. The problem is that virtually all homing missiles will be required to acquire the MBT at ranges considerably greater than this.

The percentage of the beam observation area occupied by the tank, at a given range, will of course depend on the angle of approach of the missile. It is clear, therefore, that the MMW homing head cannot 'image' the target in the sense that an optical or IR sensor is able to do. The tracking function must be performed by detection of the variation of the total reflected energy, which is observed by the monopulse beam cluster as the boresight of the antenna alters with respect to the direction of the target. Clutter in the resolution cell will contribute to this energy and is a potential source of error, unless it can be eliminated by other signal processing. Similar distortion will result whether amplitude, phase, or hybrid monopulse techniques are employed. The added sophistication of electronic beam deflection may be looked into for future systems.

The all important topic of target isolation from background clutter and the rejection of false targets must now be considered. The use of Doppler resolution, excellent against airborne targets, is of limited value for anti-tank homing missiles as the rate of change of range which produces the frequency shift is contributed mainly by the approach velocity of the missile itself. This is particularly true of missiles with a steep angle of descent. The use of differential velocity between stationary clutter and a moving tank may, however, be of some use against armour on the move, especially if sophisticated frequency domain processing is needed in the missile for other reasons.

Range gating is also of great importance. The length of the resolution cell of a radar of pulse width τ is $(c\tau/2)$, and the receiver bandwidth required to accept such a pulse is about $1/\tau$. As the velocity of light is 3×10^8 m/s or 300 m/μs, a gate of 150 m is equivalent to a pulse of 1 μs and a bandwidth of 1 MHz. To establish a gate length shorter than the physical extent of the tank, an equivalent pulse width of, say, 1 m is suitable, though a smaller range resolution would be highly desirable. This demands a bandwidth of 150 MHz. The high MMW carrier frequency of 94 GHz allows the use of this large spread of frequency. Indeed bandwidths as high as 500 MHz have been used in trial systems. This corresponds to range resolution of 0.3 m. Such range resolution raised the possibility of obtaining a range profile, or crude range image of the target. The fundamental requirement for good range resolution is wide bandwidth rather than short pulse length. Thus good range resolution may be obtained by pulse compression, as described in Chapter 3, making use of frequency modulated continuous wave (FMCW) or other spread spectrum transmitters. There is an added attraction for this method as MMW power sources are limited in their peak power ability at the present stage of development.

Other means of segregating the MBT from similar objects are under intense investigation. In general these techniques involve the way in which targets modify the incident signal on reflection. The signal processing module in the homing eye must perform a rapid cross correlation between the transmitted and received signals and match the result against a library of possible object signatures held in the computer memory.

Details of these signal processing systems are at the moment the subject of both national and commercial classification, but in the light of current state of the art and of theoretical considerations, it is likely that the following will be relevant:

- Examination of the target angular glint and characteristics by time domain or frequency domain analysis or both.
- Self power spectral analysis of the return signal (or autocorrelation).
- Examination of Doppler shift in time and frequency.
- Comparison of polarisation alteration by the target for various incident polarisation transmissions.

All these target signature factors may change with time as the geometrical relations between target and missile alter. The time constants of the target, particularly the wallow as it moves across rough ground, will appear in some form in the reflected signal. Analysis of the above may demand a large computer capacity, which may be readily available in a development laboratory. To produce a viable homing missile, the essential signal processing must be compressed and perhaps modified to enable it to be carried in the production missiles. The resulting system must have a high kill probability to justify the large development and provision cost.

Figure 8.7 shows a typical MMW homing head antenna. This particular system uses the twist Cassegrain technique, discussed in Chapter 4.

FIG. 8.7   Prototype millimetric wavelength *(Courtesy Marconi Defence Systems)*

Passive Radar Homing Missiles

As mentioned in Chapter 1, the word radar originated as an acronym for radio detection and ranging in the United States during the Second World War. This soon replaced the original British name of radio location. Recently the word radar has come to be used to cover all forms of sensor depending on the reception of electromagnetic radiation including optical and IR laser systems. Passive radar is a system relying on natural energy emitted by or reflected by an object of interest. Thermal imaging (TI) systems, described in Volume 8 on Surveillance and Target

Acquisition Systems, are in extensive use. These passive sensors receive thermal energy in the atmospheric windows from 3–5 μm and 8–13 μm. Passive MMW radars or radiometers operate in the 94 GHz spectral band. The energy flux from the targets is much less than that available to TI sensors but the use of superheterodyne reception renders cooling of the receiver unnecessary. The reception bandwidth is wider than is usual with active radar. Some trials have been carried out to assess the value of such a sensor in a homing missile.

Munition diameters are unlikely to be large enough to permit angular imaging, and range gating is not possible with a passive system. The lock on range for an MBT is too short for most operational needs. However, better terminal accuracy may be achieved than for active sensors owing to an absence of glint. There may therefore be some future for a MMW homing head which has an active phase followed by a passive run in to the target. No impending systems of this type are reported at the moment.

Tank Automatic Defence Radar

A new type of radar likely to appear shortly in tank warfare will now be considered. There is as yet no generally accepted name for this type of system but it will be called here the tank automatic defence radar (TADR). The concept is well known in naval warfare where the defence of a high value surface ship is partly provided by a rapid fire small calibre gun system automatically activated when a missile threat is detected and located by a sentinel radar. Examples of these are the *Phalanx* and the *Goalkeeper* systems. It is this concept that is likely to be applied to the survival of MBTs.

There exists a formidable array of anti-tank weapons. These are covered in detail in Volume 1 on Guided Weapons, but for the purpose of this chapter they may be grouped as follows:

- Those launched from a platform which has a line of sight (LOS) to the tank and consequently from the tank to the hostile platform. These high velocity projectiles fired from enemy tank guns, missiles on LOS trajectories, and lock on before launch (LOBL) homing missiles. Helicopter launched systems and those involving parachute carried munitions may also be incorporated in this group.
- Weapons which give no warning of approach. These are represented by lock on after launch (LOAL) passive homing missiles with a plunging trajectory, probably using IR homing or optical fibre control.
- Weapons which give an alerting signal in the direction of the target, which may be detected by radar warning receivers, as discussed in Chapter 9, or laser detectors. Active homing missiles, beam riding missiles, and systems using laser or MMW designators are examples of these.
- Short range munitions, tube launched by infantry from behind cover.

In the light of the above systems, the function of the TADR is to detect and locate the incoming threat projectile of the missile, and to initiate the appropriate tank defence response in sufficient time to prevent the destruction of the tank. All the above groups must be considered, although those in group C need not be included if other alerting instrumentation is provided.

The nature of the defensive response must be considered as this will have a definitive requirement on the time between radar alert and the result of the counter action. The more important of these, in increasing order of the time required for effective action, are advanced forms of reactive armour, fast firing specialised guns or missiles, deployment of decoys, making a screen of smoke or chaff, action against the hostile launch platform by the main gun or otherwise and if possible before it takes action itself and finally avoiding movement of the tank. Taking heed of these characteristics a tentative initial specification of the TADR may be suggested as follows:

- As near upper hemisphere cover as possible with maximum range of 6 km.
- Some form of rugged antenna such as an armoured slotted array on the top of the tank.
- Both range and Doppler target discrimination.
- Angle location of incoming munitions to one degree or better.
- Very short minimum range ability, 5–10 m, implying short pulse.
- Ability to locate multiple attack, implying a multi-beam array antenna.
- Some form of threat recognition.
- Automatic operation with alarm type interface with the crew.
- If possible LPI transmission.
- Ability to integrate with laser warning receivers (LWR) and laser warning detectors.

A modified version of this specification would certainly be needed as soon as experience in the design and field trials of this new type of radar became available.

Conclusion

This chapter has presented an array of systems which use radar on the battlefield. Rapid changes are taking place in the technology applied to old applications and many new operational requirements are being met by modern radar. A number of new systems may be expected to enter service in the near future. The development of MMW components working at even higher frequencies may well reveal new system possibilities.

As with many other items of military equipment, radars are becoming so expensive and complex that international consortia of commercial firms rather than individual companies or nations are becoming the norm for their development and production. As further mentioned in Chapter 9, there is a strong possibility that a new generation of radar, working on an entirely new concept, that of target environment correlation, may be imminent. If so, many new applications may be expected.

9

Electronic Warfare

Introduction

EW is an extensive subject. There is considerable literature available at all levels of technical and tactical sophistication. Thus it is necessary, in this chapter, to be both selective and brief. Further information may be found in Volume 1 on Guided Weapons and Volume 8 on Battlefield Surveillance.

EW is usually considered to include tactical and strategic use of all forms of sensor including radar IR, optical, and in space, ultraviolet (UV) surveillance, together with guidance, and fuzing systems. All communication systems are also of great importance across the frequency spectrum and can be carried by free space propagation, wire cable, or optical fibre.

This chapter will be confined to non-communication EW concerning LOS radar systems using carrier wavelengths lying approximately between 1 mm (300 GHz) and 3 m (0.1 GHz). It will be further constrained to cases where either the radar or its target is located on the surface of the battlefield. The use of physical attack of radars is considered by some to be part of EW. Such attack may take the form of infantry action, ARM, damage lasers, artillery bombardment or air attack. These methods will not be discussed here.

The following section will consider the general principles of EW applied to radar, much of which is of application not only to all or most of the radars appearing in this book but also radar in other warfare operations such as naval, air or space combat. The technical and tactical aspects of EW cannot be neatly separated, but in general the technical considerations are similar for all radar systems, whereas the tactics of EW are special to the particular type of operation, and must be closely integrated with non-radar EW activity.

General Principles of Radar Electronic Warfare

The main activities of EW are formally defined by the following groups. These will be briefly stated. Each will then be discussed in greater detail. The wording of these definitions is that of the author and differs from that of NATO in text but not significantly in concept:

- ESM (electronic support measures). These are activities which largely by the use of highly specialised receiving systems listening to enemy transmissions, provide technical and tactical data on enemy equipment and action.

- ECM (electronic countermeasures). Action to frustrate the use by the enemy of the electromagnetic spectrum, in this case the use of radar, or ESM systems.
- ECCM (electronic counter countermeasures). Action to negate the use by the enemy of ECM or ESM.

All these may be involved at the design stage of equipment where ESM is closely related to technical intelligence, in planning for operations, or on a microsecond by microsecond basis during combat.

Electronic Support Measures

Design of ESM and ELINT (electronic intelligence) systems makes full use of the latest technology. For obvious reasons the capability of actual equipments is in most cases not available for publication. The general methods and techniques employed are, however, well known.

Leaving aside non-radar signals, which complicate the design problem, the modern radar environment on the battlefield may present many thousands of pulses per second (PPS) with additional emissions from CW radars. Until quite recently, the frequency spectrum covered by most ESM equipment was 1–20 GHz, but the rapid developments in the MMW range now require that this should be extended to include at least some segments of the spectrum up to 100 GHz. The regions of particular interest are those around the atmospheric windows at 35 GHz and 94 GHz. The absorption band at 60 GHz may also be used for short range systems such as fuzes. 94 GHz is of special importance to RWR for tanks as anti-tank homing missiles and smart munitions are expected to work in this band.

ESM search systems must cover wide spatial arcs in azimuth and elevation depending on their particular operational use. Many of the radars to be detected will have scanning antennas with narrow beams. In such cases the ESM receiver must maintain reception sensitivity in the direction of the radar for long enough to observe the main beam if the probability of intercept is to be kept high. For some purposes the polar plot of the antenna of a radar may be required, and if this is so the ESM receiver needs sufficient sensitivity to measure the time variable signal as the victim radar antenna rotates.

Some modern radars use polarisation diversity. If these are to be detected by an ESM system it will be necessary to provide it with antennas capable of receiving two orthogonal polarisation radar transmissions, such as horizontal and vertical, or both right hand and left hand CP.

The time profile of a victim radar transmission is of great importance. The time epoch over which its amplitude variation is required must be considered carefully in relation to the radar characteristics which are to be determined. Fluctuations over a time of the order of a few cycles of the carrier frequency will usually be measured by frequency domain instrumentation. These will include such data as the carrier frequency, modulation of frequency or phase to provide pulse compression, and pulse to pulse frequency agility. A longer time window corresponding to the pulse length will reveal envelope modulation of the pulses. This may be extended to observe pulse groups, short relative to the basic pulse repetition interval. A time frame long enough to encompass several pulses or pulse groups will give information about the PRF and the nature of any jitter or periodic fluctuation. Rather longer time frames must be observed to provide scan times and antenna polar diagram plots. All the preceding data allows analysis of the radar technical capability to be carried out by the ESM computer.

On a much longer time scale the ESM system can log the activity of the victim radar on a minute by minute, hour by hour, or even day by day basis. This type of information is likely to supply tactical rather than technical information. Where several radars work as a group, ESM systems can identify the units or weapon sites that use them.

Tactical Aspects of ESM

Perhaps the simplest application of ESM is the use of receivers to alert the crew of a vehicle that they are under observation by enemy radar. A lightweight equipment suitable for mounting on helicopters or winged aircraft is shown in Figure 9.1. This system not only provides warning but also indicates the direction of the threat radar and can, if required, trigger suitable ECM, such as those discussed later in this chapter. A type of system for tracked or wheeled vehicles is shown in Figure 9.2.

In the intense EW duel which is likely to take place between aircraft flying at high speed and medium to high altitude above areas defended by surface-to-air guided weapons (SAGW), more elaborate equipment may be required which is able to identify the type of enemy radar. This allows the crew to be warned of specific threats as soon as the radar signals are detected. Such systems would be constructed to respond to both ground based and airborne radars. They are available in both pod form and as part of the permanent fit of the aircraft. In many systems they are integrated with automatic airborne self-protection jammers.

A modern example of the use of ESM tactics is shown in Figure 9.3. Two UMAs are employed to find out the location, radar characteristics and speed of response of enemy SAGW. The lower UMA has an artificially enhanced RCS to emulate a ground attack aircraft. When the enemy SAGW starts to engage it, the higher UMA records the details of the ground radars, and may instantly transmit these details to its base or to an airborne control platform. The small and relatively inexpensive UMA may be considered expendable or they may be able to return to base.

Certain operations may permit a highly sophisticated ESM station. These may need some time to deploy, and may remain at a given location for some time. In many cases large multi-channel equipments, used in conjunction with other stations, may be employed, allowing location of transmitters by triangulation. Such systems are costly and require skilled operators. A hypothetical system is shown in block diagram form in Figure 9.4.

ESM vs Radar Confrontation

The outcome of the electronic battle between an ESM receiver mounted in an aircraft and a ground radar can be predicted by use of the appropriate range equations. Here important factors such as receiver bandwidths and pulse

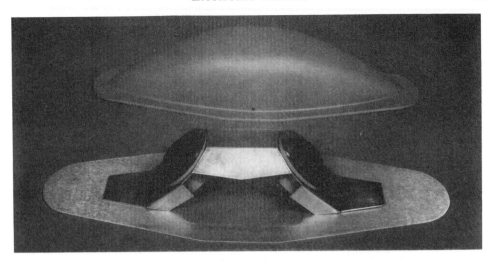

FIG. 9.1   *Prophet* radar threat warner: (a) antennas with radome, (b) display and
control unit *(Courtesy Racal Radar Defence Systems Ltd)*

FIG. 9.2 *Sentry* land based ESM systems *(Courtesy Marconi Defence Systems)*

integration are neglected to allow a simplified calculation. The radar received power is given by:

$$S_1 = \frac{W_R}{4\pi R^2}\frac{\sigma}{4\pi R^2}A_R \text{ W}$$

where W_R is the radar effective radiated power (ERP), given by $W_R = P_t G$, where P_t is the radiated power and G is the peak antenna gain. R is the range radar to aircraft (metres), σ is the aircraft RCS (m^2) and A_R is the effective aperture of the radar antenna (m^2).

The power received by an ESM receiver in the aircraft is given by:

$$S_2 = \frac{W_R}{4\pi R^2}A_S \text{ W}$$

where A_S is the ESM antenna aperture (m^2). The ESM to radar power ratio is:

FIG. 9.3   An example of modern ESM tactics

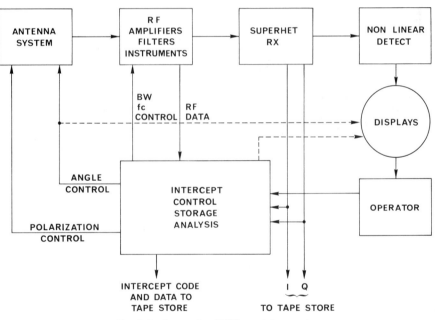

FIG. 9.4   A complex ESM receiving system

$$\frac{S_2}{S_1} = \frac{A_S 4\pi R^2}{A_R \sigma}.$$

This can be further simplified by putting $\sigma = 4\pi$ m² (a large aircraft) and $S_2/S_1 = 1$ for critical point of win or lose. Above this critical range the power into the ESM receiver is greater than the power into the radar and the aircraft will detect the radar before the radar detects it. The critical range is given by:

$$R_c = \sqrt{\frac{A_R}{A_S}}.$$

This is true even for the case where the radar antenna gain exceeds that of the ESM antenna by a factor of 10^4 (40 dB). In this case the ESM receiver will detect the radar before the radar detects the aircraft for all ranges larger than 100 m. High atmospheric attenuation will further improve the success of the ESM system.

Antenna Systems for ESM

The particular requirements for ESM systems have led to the development of a number of special types of antenna particularly suited to that task. The need to cover a very wide range of frequencies, the possibility of many different polarisation modes and the uncertainty of the direction of arrival of the incident energy must be considered in the design of such systems. There are many types of design, which vary in their suitability for various tasks. These are too numerous to describe here, but a selection of such antennas is shown in Figure 9.5. Many of

FIG. 9.5   Examples of ESM antennas *(Courtesy AEL Industries Inc)*

these have elements consisting of a spiral or helical configuration which possess the circular symmetry which allows them to respond to diverse polarisation modes and a wide range of wavelengths.

Electronic Countermeasures

ECM, the activity to impede the use by the enemy of the electromagnetic spectrum, may be divided into the following groups.

$$\left. \begin{array}{l} \text{Active (Jamming)} \\ \text{Passive} \\ \text{Tactical (Organisational)} \end{array} \right\} \text{To achieve} \left\{ \begin{array}{l} \text{Confusion} \\ \text{Deception} \\ \text{Concealment} \end{array} \right.$$

In order to obtain the most effective results it is often necessary to use all the above methods together. Jamming involves the transmission of signals of sufficient power to confuse or deceive the enemy receivers. Passive ECM has many forms but in most cases involves the use of false targets or decoys, often combined with tactical ploys. Tactical ECM usually means the planned use of active and passive methods in space, time and frequency, as well as covert movement of the troops or vehicles the enemy wishes to observe. Active deception involves the purposeful injection of false information into an enemy radar by suppression of the true signal using a stronger jamming signal transmitted from a repeater jammer.

Passive deception is often achieved by seducing the selection circuits of a radar by the creation of false targets, initially near the true targets in angle, range and/or Doppler shift, but of larger RCS. These substitute targets then draw the radar away from the actual target by movement in space or frequency at a rate similar to that of the real target. Concealment, camouflage or stealth may be achieved by careful construction of the objects the enemy wishes to detect. This may be done by the selection of special materials and by shaping the object to reduce reflection of energy towards the radar. The emission of radar smoke or black chaff may be successful in hiding the target. The tactical employment of ground or other natural screens is also of great importance.

Active Jamming

Consideration must first be given to the location of the jammer relative to the victim radar in the domains of frequency, polarisation, time and space. In order to obtain success against a radar the jammer must transmit jamming power of sufficient level within the frequency band of the radar receiver. This may be detected from the output signature of the radar if the jammer is equipped with a 'put-on' ESM receiver. If these data are not available the jamming must be spread or rapidly swept over the region of spectral uncertainty of the frequency domain containing the radar signal. Modern radars may use frequency agility or spread spectrum techniques which will add to the complexity of the jammer design. The polarisation of the jammer antenna should ideally be the same as that of the radar receiving antenna, but must not be orthogonal to it. If doubt exists as to the polarisation of the radar, the jammer needs to split its power between two antennas of orthogonal polarisation, in which case half the jamming power will be ineffective.

In the time domain the jamming signal must usually enter the radar receiver at the same time as the radar signal, or shortly before it, for optimum results. In the case of a pulse radar, jamming energy will be wasted if it is transmitted continuously, though in many systems the simplification of the jammer and its ESM put-on receiver which results from the use of continuous jamming permits a considerable reduction in jammer cost. This is particularly true in the case of simple noise jammers. Certain types of repeater jammer rely on the injection of false signals in the inter-pulse interval.

The above consderations are almost exclusively concerned with the technical design of the jammer. However, when the question of the spatial location of the jammer relative to the radar is addressed, it is of considerable significance to tactical as well as technical operation. In terms of angular position the jammer may be in the main beam of the radar, in the periphery of the main beam or in the sidelobes. In terms of range from the radar, the jammer may be at the range of the target, beyond the target or closer than the target.

Jammers at target range may be target borne jammers (TBJ), escort jammers where the jammer is carried on a platform moving with the target of interest to the radar, or dump jammers which are ejected from the target or its escort. When dump jammers, which are expendable, are released, they usually remain near the target for a short time only. Dump jammers may also be provided with a delayed start facility, in which case the jamming will come from a range other than that of the target.

Jammers situated beyond the target are stand off jammers (SOJ). These are often noise jammers which provide a noisy background against which the radar has difficulty in detecting the target. In the case of airborne jammers, a circus of jamming aeroplanes flies round a race track so placed as to frustrate radar operation against incoming attack aircraft. Figure 9.6 shows this concept. In a big

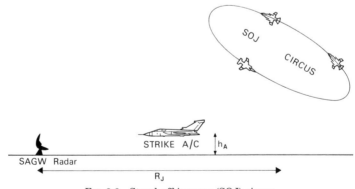

FIG. 9.6   Stand off jammer (SOJ) circus

operation the circus might contain 20 or more jamming aeroplanes in a track many tens of kilometres long. Individual aeroplanes land to refuel and then return to continue jamming.

Jammers may also be situated near to their victim radar. These are known as stand in jammers (SIJ) or stand forward jammers. Acting at short range they do not require much power and may be carried in small UMA or may be projected towards the radar from guns, mortars or rockets.

The effective life of SIJ will probably be short, as they will be located and destroyed by the forces operating the victim radar. They are therefore only suitable for short, sharp tactical engagements, in most cases. Typically they may be used by ground attack aircraft, faced with radar directed SAGW, for defence suppression.

Active Jammer—Radar Power Flight

A vital aspect of active ECM is the ratio of the target signal power to the jamming signal power in the radar receiver. This power conflict for different confrontations will now be considered.

The ratio of the radar signal power to the jamming power at the radar receiver S/J will depend on a number of factors, all of which must be considered in the detailed design of either a radar or a jammer. In order to illustrate the principles involved in different operational conditions, the more important of these factors only will be discussed here. It will be assumed that in the case of a search radar the jammer can defeat the radar if the $S/J = K$, where K is unity or less than unity, that is the jamming signal is equal to or greater than the reflected radar signal from the target. This may also be stated by assuming K is 0 dB. Actual values for this critical ratio will be a closely guarded secret for a particular military radar but, if this is available, adjustment to the calculations is easily made. In the case of tracking radars K must be much larger as the data sought is greater. A factor of 100/1 (20 dB) for K may be assumed as a trial value although lower values may be used in practical systems. Those cases where a tracking radar is involved will be considered first.

Tracking Radar v Threat Borne Jammer Confrontation

The following gives a simple quantitative example of this case. The power into the radar from the target is given by:

$$S = \frac{W_R}{4\pi R^2} \frac{\sigma}{4\pi R^2} A_R \text{ Watts}$$

where W_R is the ERP of radar (watts), R is the radar to target range (m), σ is the RCS of target (m²) and A_R is the radar antenna aperture (m²).

The power into the radar from the jammer is given by:

$$J = \frac{W_J}{4\pi R^2} A_R \text{ Watts}$$

The ratio of target to jammer power is:

$$\frac{S}{J} = \frac{W_R}{W_J} \frac{\pi}{4\pi R^2} = \frac{W_R}{W_J} \frac{1}{R^2}$$

assuming $\sigma = 4\pi$. If the jamming becomes successful when this ratio is less than 100, the burn through range R_B is given by:

$$R_B = \sqrt{\frac{W_R}{K W_J}} = \frac{1}{10} \sqrt{\frac{W_R}{W_J}}.$$

At ranges larger than this the radar will be jammed. For large radar and a small jammer, W_R/W_J could be 10^8 giving a burn through range of 1,000 m.

Here the jammer is essentially in the main beam of the radar, and the radar to target range R is the same as that to the jammer. If the jammer emits noise jamming it should cover the noise bandwidth of the radar, which in the case of a pulse tracking radar may well be larger than $1/\tau$ where τ is the pulse length, typically about 1 μs.

The equation given above shows that when the ratio $S/J = K$, there is a value of the range above which the jammer denies range data to the radar and below which the jammer is ineffective. This critical range is known as the burn through range. Note that in equations such as these it is sometimes convenient to assume a target RCS of 4π m^2. This simplifies the equation, and any other target area can readily be substituted if it is required to calculate actual quantitative values.

When such a jammer defeats the range gate of the radar it is open to the radar to use passive track on jam (TOJ) to obtain angular data. The jammer may be more effective if it operates in the repeater jamming mode.

Tracker v Repeater Target Borne Jammer

A repeater jammer is essentially associated with a receiver which can respond to the transmissions of the victim radar. A commonly used strategy is to employ gate stealing or range gate pull off (RGPO). The jammer faced with a range gated pulse tracker initially returns an exact copy of the skin echo from the target, in the case of a TBJ the reflection of its own platform. This signal is sent back immediately after the receipt of the radar pulse. During the next few pulses the jamming signal is returned with increasing amplitude. The radar signal processing circuit accepts the jamming pulses as true reflections and reduces the gain of the radar receiver as the jammer pulses grow in magnitude. The jammer must of course have sufficient power to outmatch the radar ERP. The radar receiver is now too insensitive to detect the true signals and the jammer has 'captured' the radar range gate. The jammer now delays the return of the successive radar pulses by a growing period so that the range gate becomes adjusted to accept progressively greater range reflections. When the range gate has been seduced to a false range many gate widths beyond the true target, the jammer ceases transmission. The radar is now left without a signal and must carry out a range search, during which time its angle circuits are inactive. The jammer repeats the whole process as soon as it detects that the radar has re-established track. The entire sequence described above takes place in a time frame corresponding to a few pulses of the radar. The overall result is that the radar never attains steady track of the target. Against radars with a constant PRF the jammer can simulate false targets at a reduced range as the jamming pulse can be sent just before the arrival of the next radar pulse. This cannot be done if the radar uses jittered PRF.

In some cases, radar trackers employ CW transmission, and isolate the wanted target by its Doppler shift, using a velocity gate. SAGW systems using semi-active homing are common examples of these trackers. Gate stealing in such cases is achieved by velocity gate pull off (VGPO). The concept is similar to that for RGPO but the frequency gate is seduced by the jammer sliding the returned signal in frequency instead of time. Figure 9.7 shows the block diagram of a complex repeater jammer.

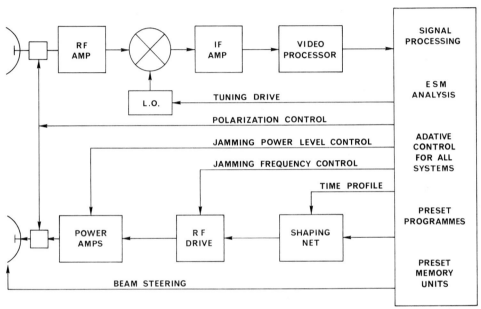

FIG. 9.7   Block diagram of complex repeater jammer

Tracking Radar v Sidelobe Jammer

The power into the radar from the target is given by:

$$S = \frac{W_R}{4\pi R_1^2} \frac{\sigma}{4\pi R_1^2} A_{R1}$$

The power into the radar from the jammer is given by:

$$J = \frac{W_R}{4\pi R_2^2} A_{R2}$$

The ratio of target to jamming power is given by:

$$\frac{S}{J} = \frac{W_R}{W_J} \frac{\sigma R_2^2}{4\pi R_1^4} \frac{A_{R1}}{A_{R2}}$$

where A_{R1} is the radar antenna aperture towards the target (m), A_{R2} is the radar antenna aperture towards the jammer (m), R_1=radar to target range (m) and R_2=radar to jammer range (m). The (R_2^2/R_1^4) factor will give the jammer a progressively increasing advantage. As it operates near to the radar the low sidelobe levels tend to protect the radar from jamming.

As seen in the above the S/J calculation is similar to that of the TBJ. The magnitude of the radar signal is the same as before for a target at the same range, R_1. However the jammer is now on a separate platform at a different range, R_2, which is greater than the target range for a stand off sidelobe jammer (SLJ) and less for a SIJ. The receiving aperture of the radar presented to the jammer is much less than that seen by a jammer in the main beam. Thus a jammer faced with sidelobe levels 20 dB down on main beam would need an ERP 20 dB greater to maintain the jamming signal strength at a radar at the same range. An additional difficulty for the SLJ is that the sidelobes of an antenna may have a polarisation that differs from that of the main beam.

A peripheral jammer, that is a jammer located close to the edge of the main beam, may be considered in the same way, but the reduction of the antenna gain is likely to be less than for an SLJ. Such jammers are effective against radar homing missiles where the jammer platform is likely to be an escort jammer.

Jammer Attack on Angle Circuits

Where a tracking radar uses a temporal scanning beam, such as a conical scan or a fan scan, to establish accurate angle tracking, an effective jamming ploy is to return a copy of the radar transmitted signal but with a periodic amplitude modulation of the return at the frequency of the scan. The phase of this modulation should differ from that producing the error signal in the radar. The resulting mixed true and false pulses are processed by the angle circuits of the radar to give an error signal of the wrong phase. This signal applied to the servos of the radar causes the antenna to move off the target. In the case of a radar using electronic scan, faulty beam steering will result. This type of jamming is called con scan jam or fan scan jam. In some jammers noise transmissions are modulated at the scan frequency.

To an increasing degree, modern military radars are using static split methods (monopulse) to give angle data, largely as a result of the success of modulated jamming. Several different methods of jamming monopulse systems have been suggested, and extensive trials have been carried out, but it seems that effective jamming at reasonable power levels is difficult to provide. Powerful noise jamming is available to defeat range or velocity gates, but the radar may switch to TOJ. This is discussed further in the later section on ECCM. The use of decoys of some form is likely to be more effective than active jamming, against static split trackers.

Passive ECM, Decoys and Chaff

A radar decoy is a false target deliberately deployed by the enemy to deceive or confuse the radar which is operating against him. It must have similar reflective properties as the true target, but usually with a larger RCS so as to present a more attractive signal to the radar.

When used against a tracking radar or homing missile the decoy may be ejected from the target to seduce the tracker away. The most effective moment to produce the decoy is at the time the radar is trying to establish lock on the target, but an effective decoy may be able to break lock which has already been achieved. In this case the decoy starts in the same resolution cell as the target in angle, range and Doppler, but as soon as the radar has transferred its attention to the decoy, the radar is led away from the target in one or more domains. The most effective systems do not produce such a large deflection of the radar at once that the radar is alerted of the deception. The most usual displacement of the target from the decoy is to remove the decoy from the target physically by relative movement between the two. In the case of decoys deployed by high speed aircraft, a Doppler gap rapidly develops as the decoy adopts the speed of the surrounding air, unless a powered vehicle carries the decoy. The target must have some way of knowing the best time to release its decoys.

Decoys may be used in many ways against search, acquisition or surveillance radars. In the case of stationary assets on the battlefield, many decoys may be placed round the true target to confuse the enemy as to the actual number of equipments present. The valuable asset may also be 'lost in the crowd' of cheap decoys. In the past complete air fields have been simulated by the use of arrays of decoys. Incoming radar homing missiles attacking tanks or aircraft may be accompanied by several decoys, constructed to resemble the missile, if the cost justifies this.

When a particularly elaborate target has to be simulated it may be necessary to provide the decoy with transmitters to mimic the signature of the true target. In Chapter 8 the current research into methods of identifying MBTs by MMW homing was discussed. It is clear that the information gleaned by the signal processing adopted may be corrupted by suitable constructed decoys. The development of such techniques lies in the future.

One of the most commonly used forms of decoy is chaff, also known as duppel or window. The calculation below indicates the target signal to chaff signal ratio when the resolution cell of the radar is filled with chaff. The chaff itself consists of large numbers of strips of light plastic substrate metallised to present a cloud of reflective dipoles of approximately one half of the radar wavelength. Chaff clouds can be produced by dispensing bundles of dipoles from an aircraft, or firing them into position by a gun, mortar or compressed air launcher. Where the requirement is for decoy action against several different types of radar, a 'cocktail' consisting of a bundle of dipoles of many different lengths may be used, but modern trends indicate the use of small but carefully positioned clouds.

The Influence of Chaff on a Tracking Radar

The power into the radar from a target at range Rm from radar is:

$$S_t = \frac{W_R}{4\pi R^2} \frac{\sigma}{4\pi R^2} A_R \ \text{W.}$$

The volume of the resolution cell around the target is given by:

$$V = \frac{R\theta R\phi c\tau}{2} \ \text{m}^3$$

where θ is the elevation beamwidth (radians), ϕ is the azimuth beamwidth (radians), τ is the pulse length (seconds) and c is the velocity of light (m/s). The RCS σ_c of a cell filled with chaff of specific RCS σ_0 m² per m³ is

$$\sigma_c = \frac{R\theta R\phi c\theta}{2}\, \sigma_0 \text{ m}^2.$$

The ratio of power from the target and chaff is given by:

$$\frac{S_t}{S_c} = \frac{W_R \sigma A_R}{16\pi^2 R^4}\, \frac{32\pi^2 R^4}{W_R R^2 \theta \phi c \tau \sigma_0 A_R}$$

so that

$$\frac{S_t}{S_c} = \frac{2\sigma}{R^2 \theta \phi c \tau_0}.$$

It is thus clear that the radar should aim for narrow beams and short pulses to minimise the effect of chaff. Increased power does not improve the target to chaff signal ratio.

ECM Directed Against Surveillance or Acquisition Radars

In the following section the EW activity will be related to a surface-to-air surveillance radar using a rotating beam in bearing with electronic elevation scan. The principles discussed may be readily adjusted to cover other types of surveillance radar.

The purpose of such a radar is to detect targets within its coverage volume, to determine their trajectories and location, and, when required, to pass such data to weapon systems. They are usually coupled to an identification system (IFF).

The use of self-protection active jamming by potential targets against this type of radar is unusual as the jamming would act as a beacon which might be detected by the radar even beyond its own coverage range, provided an LOS from target to radar existed.

However, powerful noise jamming from special aircraft remaining at long range SOJ may be used to mask the target echo from targets entering the observation zone. The concept of the SOJ circus has already been discussed. The presence of random noise jamming has the effect of raising the antenna noise temperature, thus reducing the detectability of all targets. If the radar employs CFAR detection, the detection probability of all targets will be progressively reduced as the jamming power rises. If CFAR is not used the targets will be masked by many false alarms. As the radar antenna scans in bearing and elevation, the noise power entering the radar will vary as the effective antenna aperture presented to the jamming aircraft changes. A jammer of given ERP will have greater effect the nearer it is to the victim radar, but it will then be vulnerable to attack by anti-aircraft defences associated with the radar. Such close in jamming is likely to be emitted from small UMA or expendable jammers dumped by parachute or fired from a gun or rocket system. The following section explains the effect of propagation loss on SOJ systems.

Effect of Propagation Loss on Stand off Jammers

For a target at range R_1 and a SOJ at range R_2 in the main beam of a radar, the ratio of power from the target and jammer is given by:

$$\frac{S}{J} = \frac{W_R}{W_J} \frac{\sigma R_2^2}{4\pi R_1^4}$$

assuming no propagation loss. For a propagation loss of $e^{-\alpha R}$ for a path length R (one way loss) this equation must be modified to:

$$\frac{S}{J} = \frac{W_R \sigma R_2^2 C^{-2R_1 \alpha}}{W_J 4\pi R_1^4 C^{-R_2 \alpha}} = \frac{W_R \sigma R_2^2}{W_J 4\pi R_1^4} e^{-\alpha(2R_1 - R_2)}$$

where the value of the constant α is related to the propagation loss in dB per m.

It is clear that atmospheric attenuation will help the jammer if it is nearer to the radar than twice the target range but for SOJ beyond this range propagation loss will favour the radar. This advantage may be exploited.

Repeater Jamming used Against Surveillance Radars

If a single repeater jammer is able to inject a signal of such strength into a radar as to simulate the main beam target echo when the radar antenna is in such a position that the minimum level of its polar diagram is directed towards the jamming platform, then the repeater jammer can manipulate the power level of the jamming pulses returned to the radar so that the radar display or memory store is presented with a false target. This type of confusion is called inverse gain, or angle ghost jamming. The power required by the jammer is considerable, or it must operate close to the victim radar. It would not be effective against a radar using random scan.

Use of Chaff Against Surveillance Radars

In the past chaff has been used on a grand scale to produce massive tactical deception by simulating the approach of apparent airborne and seaborne forces. The notable occasion on which this was successfully applied was during the invasion of Normandy. It was also used to conceal large scale air attacks over Germany, and later it has been reported that extensive use of chaff accompanied the movement of Soviet forces into Hungary. The employment of these methods could be mounted in the future but the results would probably be less effective than in the past due to the increased awareness of the tactics of EW, and the much improved ECCM now available. The greatly increased use of MTI or fully implemented frequency domain Doppler signal processing renders the use of chaff far less effective unless the rate of change of the chaff with respect to the radar can be matched to the range rate of the target.

Electronic Counter Countermeasures

ECCM are activities of one side in an EW conflict to frustrate or minimize the efforts of the opposing side to gain tactical advantage by the use of ECM. This ECCM action may be one or more of the following:

- The integration of EW tactical planning with other aspects of tactical staff battle preparations.
- The training of radar operators in all aspects of EW, and especially in the recognition of enemy ECM, and the methods of reducing their effect.
- The design of radar antennas to reduce the impact of enemy ECM.
- The design of radar transmitters to dominate in the power fight against specified opposing ECM.
- The design of radar receivers, particularly their signal processing, to minimise the effect of enemy confusion or deception jamming.

Tactical ECCM

It is difficult to discuss this aspect of EW without taking a specific scenario in considerable detail. This will not be attempted here, but some general points may be made. Study of past battles remains the most effective guide. Complete radar silence, where this is possible, is the most powerful ECCM of all. Coupled with effective ESM to exploit any transmissions made by the enemy, it provides tactical surprise, the paramount force multiplier. Failing total silence, the use of bistatic radar with a transmitter out of reach of the enemy enables radar receiving stations to remain covert. Tactical plans which provide the enemy with false information as to the physical location, frequency of transmission, or time of operation of essential radars can be highly effective. If resources permit, a network of radars which turn on and off for short periods, which could be as short as a few milliseconds, confront the opposing ECM forces with a difficult problem. In some circumstances it may be of value to provide radars which transmit with the deliberate intention of attracting enemy jamming. The location of the jamming stations is then revealed. It is possible also that jamming power used against such radars will rob the enemy of the ability to provide adequate jamming power against other radars located elsewhere in the space of frequency domains. As a general principle in EW, the task of the enemy ECM resources will be made more difficult by deploying radars, as widely as possible in space, in frequency and in time.

ECCM Antenna Specification

The majority of monostatic radar equipments use the same antenna for both transmission and reception. The antenna design must, therefore, be a compromise between its transmission and its reception function. From the point of view of ECCM effectiveness it is fortunate that the requirements are in most aspects similar for transmission and reception.

In the case of the classic surveillance radar with a rotating aperture, usually a reflecting final element fed by a fixed feed such as an array of horns, the main ECCM requirement is for low sidelobe levels. This impedes the enemy ESM receivers, and is also desirable in reducing the effectiveness of opposing sidelobe jammers. If possible, provision should be made to operate in two orthogonal modes of polarisation, where target scattering cross section and propagation characteristics permit this. This may help against the so-called stealth targets. It also forces the enemy to provide jamming in two orthogonal modes, which has the effect of reducing his jamming power to half for a given available power supply.

The increasing use of sophisticated array antenna systems allows the surveillance radar to resort to adaptive techniques which provide the ability to modify the polar diagram so that a null in the receiving aperture can be steered on to the direction of a jammer, thus reducing its effectiveness. Each jammer to be neutralised needs a monitoring closed loop controlling an area of array elements. This concept has been described in more detail in Chapter 4. It emphasises the general point that technical design of a radar must have a specified ECM and ESM threat to overcome. The determination of this potential threat is a very difficult decision. The development of a radar may take many years, during which time changes in the political and tactical environment may well invalidate the original specification. As always the ruggedness of the antenna against enemy physical attack must be taken into consideration.

ECCM Transmitter Specification

The first and most important requirement for a radar transmitter faced with an EW environment is that it should have sufficient power to overcome the specified jamming threat when observing the smallest and most remote target. If possible provision should be made during the design phase to allow for expansion of the power at a later stage of development, when demands for an increased threat will almost certainly occur.

In general, isolation of the target in as many ways as possible will provide the best ECCM. Given that the antenna has provided the optimum discrimination possible in two angle domains and the polarisation domain, it falls to the transmitter to provide range and velocity isolation.

These requirements are to some extent in opposition as range discrimination demands wide bandwidth transmission, while the best Doppler filtering is obtained with a narrow frequency line coupled with a long time of observation to allow the signal to grow in a narrow band filter. The design will be further complicated by the basic characteristics of the radar needed in clear conditions. The most effective transmitter from an ECCM point of view is thus an adaptive equipment which can be modified by the selection of various modes depending on the actual ECM threat it has to defeat at any given time. A likely choice, given no constraints on cost, would be a master oscillator power amplifier (MOPA) transmitting chain capable of providing wide ranging carrier frequency selection, with coherent pulses and adaptive pulse compression. Over a force containing many radars the widest possible range of available carrier frequencies should be provided apart from the frequency agility or multi-band facilities in any one radar.

ECCM Receiver Specification

In any radar the receiver design must be closely related to the nature of the transmitted waveform. When no ECM are to be expected, the receiver signal processing should be optimised to provide the best estimate of target detection, target location and/or target velocity in the presence of external noise, represented by antenna temperature and target noise, clutter competing with the target signal, and internal noise represented by the effective noise temperature of the receiver. Surveillance radars seeking maximum signal to noise ratio will be equipped with a matched filter giving the best possible detection when receiving the expected return signal in the presence of random white noise. Such receivers are already optimised to reject random noise jamming with similar statistics to the system noise and little more can be done within the receiver.

When faced with repeater jamming, recourse must be made to the fact that the false information injected by such a jammer relies on the return of the expected signal which is then modified in some respect to seduce the radar away from the target in one or more domains. Range, velocity, or angle gate stealers are examples of this. Protection may be obtained against such jammers if the characteristic movement of true targets is known. Deceptive movement of the target can then be detected by so-called guard gates, which prevent further pull off if uncharacteristic motion of the signal is identified.

Random pulse jamming, intended to produce confusion or temporary paralysis of a radar can be degraded by splitting the superheterodyne intermediate frequency (IF) amplifier into two sections separated by a limiting device. The first wide band section preserves the pulse shape of target and hostile pulses alike. The limiter constrains all pulses to the same amplitude, effectively cutting down the jamming pulse power. The second section acts as a matched filter in the normal way.

When the radar is confronted with decoys or decoy chaff the requirement is to exploit some aspect in which the decoy differs from the true target. This is essentially a pattern recognition process, and a powerful ECCM is to present a suitable display to a well trained radar operator, software to match and replace the skill of the man or woman in this context.

General ECCM Techniques

In many cases ECCM ploys involve the co-operative use of antenna, transmitter, and receiver design. An example of this is the use of lobe on receive only (LORO) to combat conical scan jamming or fan scan jamming. This method gives some measure of protection without going to the expense of replacing the angle determination receiver of a tracking radar with the three receiver processing of a monopulse system. The scanning transmitting antenna is replaced with a staring antenna which illuminates the target with a constant amplitude stream of pulses, of PRF, polarisation, and frequency matched to the receiver. This denies the enemy data on the scan characteristics of the angle gates.

In many cases ECCM performance may be improved by the use of pulse compression, which allows greater energy per pulse, and hence signal to jamming ratio, while maintaining the bandwidth needed for range discrimination. The transmitter must provide longer pulses with swept frequency or a phase switched waveform, the antenna must have the necessary bandwidth, while the receiver requires the essential pulse compression filter matched to the transmitted waveform.

Rejection of sidelobe jammers may be achieved by the use of an additional antenna with an approximate isotropic polar diagram in the plane containing the jammer. The signals may be processed by the receiver to reject signals not appearing in the main lobe of the radar which produce a stronger signal in the auxiliary antenna than in the main antenna sidelobes.

When a radar is liable to attack by an ARM which is homing on to the radar transmission, an obvious ECCM is to turn off the transmitter. Unfortunately this negates the purpose of the radar. An alternative tactic is to illuminate a patch of ground or water with a bleed from the main transmission. The desired effect is to deflect the missile so that it explodes harmlessly at some distance from the radar. This technique is sometimes called terrain bounce.

Conclusion

EW, including radar, communications, IR sensors, and optical devices is almost certain to grow in importance in the coming years. The great speed of development of technology in these areas shows no sign of abating. Vast expansion in the development of optical computing and signal processing may also be expected. Whenever new and improved methods of making and using sensors become available in the military sphere, new advances in ECM and ECCM quickly follow.

Partly as a result of the recent advances in chaos theory, there are strong indications that radically new concepts in radar systems may be expected. These are in their infancy at present, but appear to involve the cross correlation between target and its clutter environment rather than correlation between the transmitted and the received signal which is the basis of present active radar. The forms of EW activity which will evolve must await the development of the methods derived from such concepts.

10

Conclusions

The Importance of Radar in the Battlefield

Comparison with Other Surveillance and Target
Acquisition Methods

Radar is a battlefield surveillance and target acquisition (STA) method of primary importance. This book has described its operation and application and it is appropriate here to highlight its main capabilities and to place these in the context of other battlefield systems. These primary capabilities are:

- Detection of small, fast targets.
- Provision of range data.
- Long range capability.
- All weather, day and night operation.
- An ability to see through heavy smoke and the fog of battle.

Electro-optic (E-O) systems provide another important STA technique and, although both radar and E-O operate using electromagnetic energy, the vastly different wavelength used means that their characteristics are to some extent complementary. E-O systems in general have much shorter range than radar. Visual systems such as binoculars operate in daytime only, whilst image intensifiers and thermal imagers extend this to night. The relatively high resolution of E-O systems compared to radar stems directly from the difference in operating wavelength. However, some degree of imaging is possible with radar. Perhaps the most important characteristic of radar is its ability to see through rain, cloud, fog and battlefield obscurants. This factor has, for example, made millimetric radar the favoured choice over E-O for attack of second echelon armour using guided rockets or missiles.

Radar is active. Although this is a problem in many applications and leads to a wide range of countermeasures, it is one of the very properties that gives radar its outstanding range capabilities. Indeed one of its vulnerabilities is the key to its advantages and any informed comparison needs to consider this.

The ideal surveillance device would allow the operator to scan through the frequencies, and use those which are the most effective in the prevailing light, weather and battle conditions. He would then be able to move throughout the whole gamut of detection, recognition and identification, using the relevant atmospheric windows and increased imaging capability as the wavelength shortened. Unfortunately, when long range is required and the necessity arises to penetrate rain and all forms of smoke or even the smoke of battle, then longer wavelengths and active systems are necessary.

There are other methods of achieving surveillance at a distance. Remote ground sensors (RGS) can be placed, dropped or fired into position. The problem is to know exactly where they are required. Choke points on routes behind the enemy's positions are obvious choices, but these are limited in number. RPVs are now serious contenders for the task, but they must be fitted with sensors and the best all weather sensor devices in cloudy northern Europe are radars. The end result is that other sensing devices are often required, at relatively close ranges, to identify and even to recognise targets in cluttered ground conditions. In certain conditions radar can recognise targets, and with well trained, experienced operators, even identify them; but they do not have the resolution to act as a sight for a gun, which thermal imagers and image intensifiers are able to do so well. Radar, however, remains the queen of the STA devices. Only radar can reach out to the horizon, in all weathers, to detect aircraft approaching and track them accurately until they are acquired by the defensive weapon system; only radar has the range capability to detect enemy vehicles and formations moving forward at more than a few miles distance; only radar has the capability to track shells, accurately, close to their launch point and hence guide counter-battery fire.

Multiple Sensor Operation

In a battlefield environment many different types of sensor will be present, generating various forms of information. Radar has been compared with other sensors, notably E-O types, and shown to have contrasting and in some cases complementary characteristics. As hinted above it therefore seems logical to try to combine these characteristics in some way and to attempt to exploit any advantages that can be obtained from multiple sensor operation.

In its widest context, multiple sensor operation may embrace such diverse systems as satellite observation, both using radar and E-O sensors, acoustic devices, optical instruments and radar. It also involves the problem of data fusion discussed below. At another level, it matches the technique to specific problem areas such as air defence or short range battlefield surveillance.

In such cases there are a number of important factors that need to be considered. Some of these are:

- Does the combination have better STA properties at the expense of worse susceptibility to ECM? This might be the case when, for example, a radar, an active device, is combined with an optical sight, a passive device, to give all weather capability. On the other hand, to supplement a surveillance radar with a thermal imager to enhance its target recognition performance may well reduce the overall susceptibility, by reducing the radar transmission time.
- The use of multiple sensors may increase the overall sensor aperture size leading to larger and heavier equipment.
- Mutual interference must be avoided by good electromagnetic compatibility measures.

These aspects are illustrated by considering some current multiple sensor systems. The first of these is the *Rapier* air defence missile system described in Chapter 7. In its normal mode of operation the target azimuth is acquired by the surveillance radar whilst tracking is carried out optically. Although this is not a multiple sensor system in its fullest sense, as the two do not operate in parallel but rather in a serial way, it highlights the advantages and problems involved. The optical sensor is less susceptible to countermeasures but could not do the full STA job alone. The two sensors have been engineered to work together with the minimum of self-interference. The combined system is large and it would seem hard to combine it into a single piece of equipment. An interesting example of combining sensors into a single aperture is the combination of secondary and primary radar for air traffic or AD weapon control. Figure 10.1 shows how this

FIG. 10.1   Combined primary and secondary radar antenna *(Courtesy Cossor Electronics Ltd)*

can be done. The large slot array forms the narrow pencil beam of a primary radar working at a relatively high frequency, whilst the block shaped dipoles on the array face form the secondary radar antenna used for interrogating the aircraft transponder. The latter works on a much lower frequency and hence does not interfere with primary radar. Other ways of controlling likely interference are by using opposite polarisations or by time multiplexing.

A further example of multiple sensor operation is shown in Figure 10.2. This system is produced by LMT Radio Professionnelle and shows how a BSR, the *RASIT* described in Chapter 5, can be advantageously combined with a thermal camera. The relatively poor resolution of the radar is enhanced by the good image recognition properties of a camera. The camera is slaved to the radar. Upon

FIG. 10.2   Combined radar and thermal imaging system *(Courtesy LMT Radio Professionelle)*

seeing a target of interest in the lower display of the control unit, Figure 10.3, the operator can view it directly on camera screen above. However the equipment is twice as bulky and the image recognition is of course subject to good weather conditions.

Data Dissemination and Fusion

It is clear from the wide variety of radars described in this book, together with the array of other available sensor types, that there will be many STA devices operating on the battlefield. It goes without saying that these sensors are useless unless the information they generate can reach the user fast enough to be assimilated and to allow appropriate action to be taken. In many cases it is obvious who should be the recipient, and what his needs actually are, but with the ever burgeoning complexity of electronics on the battlefield this is less evident. The increasing ability to pass information from user to user is making the topic of data dissemination and fusion ever more pertinent. In this area both sensor and communication technology and deployment become an integrated study. New sensor developments must be considered when specifying communication needs, just as communications capabilities must bear on the specification of new sensors.

In purely radar terms data fusion is already a topic of active research and development. The problem addressed here is, for example, how to combine two

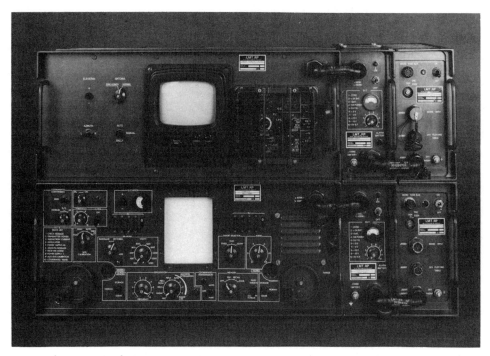

FIG. 10.3   Control unit for combined radar and thermal imaging system *(Courtesy LMT Radio Professionelle)*

tracks of the same target from adjacent surveillance radars to produce a single track. Alternatively the two tracks may be from a radar and an E-O sensor. Such a combination makes for a more accurate and reliable result. Track correlation techniques are used that may take account of the noise statistics of each source. It is obvious that this is harder when the tracks are from different sensors such as radar and E-O.

Another, more difficult problem is that of the organisation of the data dissemination from wide area sensors such as long range airborne surveillance radar, namely AWACS, *Orchidée* or ASTOR. Questions that must be answered here are who is to get the information and in what form should it be passed? Limited communication resources usually mean that as much interpretation should take place as early as possible. This would suggest that SAR type images should have skilled photo-interpreters in the aircraft ground station. Instructions on the targets of interest must be input to these ground stations to enable usable information to be output. This is less of a problem with MTI radars where the output will be co-ordinates, speed and direction of correlated moving target tracks, and the details of the entire scene may be transmitted over existing trunk data links in reasonable time. Once a data set describing the current situation has been established with every user, only updating reports will be necessary. However, having said this, it is likely that the increasing need for data communication around the battlefield for this and many other needs will put an ever heavier burden on communication resources.

The Importance of EW and its Impact on Radar

The importance of EW has long been recognised in the wider scope of radar application. The use of EW techniques in airborne radar in the Second World War established its crucial role in air warfare. Although it is applicable to all spheres of radar use, it is likely that the full impact of radar EW on the battlefield has not yet been felt. It should be emphasised, however, that radar forms an integral part of many new battlefield weapon systems, including guns and guided weapons, and EW will be applied through the weapon sensors whether they are radar, IR or optical. Many isolated radar sensors are also of high value in an EW sense. WLR and long range airborne BSR provide important information and thus are likely to be attacked with EW. The amount of electronic attack will be proportional to the degree of importance attached by the enemy to the radar data produced.

Chapter 9 has described both the organisation and techniques of EW and serves to emphasise its importance. However, in reality EW is not a stand alone concept or something that can be added to equipment after design. The EW ethos permeates the whole of the radar field, from the basic concepts through to application and employment. Indeed in many cases it also includes communications EW, as data dissemination is a key to successful sensor operation. Thus EW should be borne in mind when writing requirements for and designing both radar sensors and associated data processing and communications equipment. The likely impact on design is to increase complexity. In many cases, good radar design procedures result in hardness to EW, such as, for example, narrow antenna beamwidths giving improved resolution and increased resistance to jamming. Unfortunately, in general, building for the EW battle will make radars more expensive. Early specification of needs may alleviate this to some extent and should be done in all cases. The trend to software control is an important development that may allow future EW enhancements to be retrofitted well into the radar lifetime.

One of the key factors in EW is the power battle. Chapter 9 emphasised the ability of an ESM receiver to detect the presence of the radar before it was itself detected by the radar. Similarly an onboard jammer always has some advantage as its energy only needs to travel half the distance of the radar energy. These and other important deductions, which can be derived from the basics of radar operation, are highly significant. For instance they allow operation tactics to be developed to exploit the advantages fully. The example of an aircraft approaching an AD radar from below the horizon by flying just under its radar beam by the use of an ESM receiver, the 'lobe pecking' technique, illustrates how such methods can be exploited. And of course these deductions also allow estimation of the likely outcome of an engagement. In some cases the full use of EW may swing the advantage heavily one way or the other. In other cases small, but eventually significant, changes in effectiveness may result. However, whichever way it goes it is very clear that electronic warfare is an increasingly important aspect of battlefield radars.

The Future

Future Technical Trends

In general terms the development of phased arrays and large scale digital processing will mean that radars will have greater capability. Some specific areas of improvement include adaptive radar, the application of processing to image recognition and the use of artificial intelligence.

Adaptive Radar

Many factors affect the operation of a radar system. A radar is usually designed with a particular task in mind and the values of such characteristics as PRF, pulse duration, frequency, beam shape and peak power are usually chosen to provide the best possible results. Even so, many of the factors conflict and the design, at best, is a compromise. It may be possible in the future to create an adaptive radar, in which provision is made for changing rapidly many of the transmitter and receiver characteristics to meet varying needs. By changing the radar parameters as required a single radar system may produce satisfactory results in many roles. It could be used in the AD role to provide, for example, good probability of detection at long ranges, converting to the role of accurate tracing radar as the target closed. With such a system, ECM interference could be avoided by rapidly changing the frequency. The equipment could be used in an MTI mode or as a non-MTI radar. Frequency agility may be switched in as required. Pulse compression networks may be made available. The possibilities are obviously immense.

In one sense, however, such radars are already with us. The combined surveillance, tracking and guidance modes of the *Patriot* radar, described in Chapter 7, is an example. Others can be quoted. Further developments of this concept can be expected in the future.

Artificial Intelligence

Artificial intelligence is a topic whose scope is beyond the limits of this book, but whose all pervasive nature is likely to affect both radar design and operation. Several examples of building in intelligence to radar systems have been described in this book and are current practice. BITE and adaptive antennas are examples of 'knowledge based' intelligence where reaction to certain events occurs in a predictable and reproducible way. However, a truly intelligent system would be able to select an optimal course of action from a complex and often conflicting set of rules, not always deriving a consistent or unique action. Indeed the choice of action may have an element of learning in it provided the results or consequences of the choice can be fed back in.

An important area where intelligent systems have an increasing role to play is in target recognition. Here research has shown that images of near optical clarity can be obtained by a radar that looks at a target from many different angles, and uses many different frequencies and polarisations. However, in practice good recognition is needed from very little information. A single look angle, frequency and polarisation may be all that is available. The human brain has a very good capability of recognition of objects from sparse data. This is because the brain is composed of many million processing elements, called neurons, that work on the data in parallel. In a normal computer the processing is done serially, that is one bit after another. Work is currently under way to create computers that mimic the operation of the brain and these are called neural networks. An important feature of such a computer is that the interconnections between the many parallel processors is controlled both by the input and the output. In other words, success in a pattern recognition task can be communicated to the computer which then learns the interconnection layout associated with that type of data input. It is possible also that such artificial intelligence systems will also be applied to radar hardware design and will feature in the adaptive radars described above.

Future Military Trends

The future potential of any STA device must take in the traditional technical and tactical arguments and balances. However, as the strategic priorities change, so the weightings of the various arguments take on new values.

There has always been a school of argument that says that the greatest guarantors of peace are the spy satellites. This argument is readily extended to cover all surveillance. In the modern era of disarmament and the reduction of conventional forces, the value of surveillance devices, which double up as verification systems to ensure that the promised reductions and removals have taken place, and as part of a credible military capability should it be necessary to field fighting forces anywhere in the world, will carry a heavy weighting in their favour. Obviously, in all the roles that can be envisaged, range will be important and radar readily rears its head.

Assuming that the major military groupings succeed in agreeing to reduce their nuclear and conventional forces, it must not be overlooked that this will only be possible with a radical reorganisation of those forces. What is more, these reorganisations will be sold to general staffs, and carried out, as improvements to operational efficiency. The speed of movement and the use of helicopters will almost certainly increase. Early detection of the movement of stores and equipment, as well as the movement of military forces themselves, will become even more important than in the past.

No doubt, too, the major nations and military groupings will wish to keep an eye on what other militarily ambitious nations in the world are doing to upset the nuclear and general military balance of the world. Again, long range, early detection of indications of military changes will become necessary.

At the moment only the United States and the Soviet Union own and can deploy the assets to give a strategic cover required, but it is not beyond the technical capability of China, Japan, Europe, nor probably the apocryphal skill of the Israel/South Africa combination, to follow. At the moment the systems deploy E-O, radio and radar sensors in a mix of satellites and high flying aircraft. The SAR is capable of producing pictures, taken through the densest cloud cover, with a ground resolution of one metre.

The intelligence gained from the satellite systems will alert and allow a challenge to the opposition. The next requirement will be to maintain a closer and 24 hour watch on any developments. Both the United States and NATO use the AWACS as the next stage. This is a stand off system that uses friendly or neutral airspace. The stand off technique allows surveillance from behind the forward edge of the battle area (FEBA) or peacetime frontiers, which is flexible, unprovocative if necessary, and sensible in time of peace or war. The peacetime use of AWACS, to give confidence, has been evident already in many areas of the world.

Other, less expensive, sideways looking surveillance radar systems are under development. They range from the US joint Surveillance Target Attack Radar System (joint STARS) through the Airborne Stand Off Radar (ASTOR) programme to the French heliborne *Orchidée* system. Joint STARS is an airborne attack and surveillance system mainly designed to detect and identify moving enemy vehicles and formations out to a range of 150 km. It then has the capability to guide missiles and attack aircraft on to them.

This demonstrates the unique value of MTI radars. Only they are able to detect vehicles moving by day or night under the discipline of electronic silence. The value is equally evident for peacetime verification or for dealing with a follow-on forces attack (FOFA) if war has begun.

As yet the radars we have been considering for the future are envisaged in piloted aircraft. At their present stage of development RPVs are optimised as target acquisition vehicles and are unsuitable for mounting MTI radars or SAR. However, it is by no means inconceivable that they can be designed with the required payload and stealth aerodynamic features to make them into potent radar surveillance carriers in the future.

Unfortunately, whenever we begin to map out future plans the harsh limiting world of cash rears its head. In this case, as a look at the graph in Figure 10.4 will

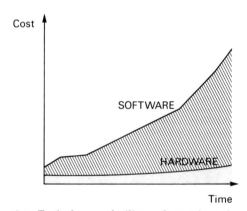

FIG. 10.4   Typical costs of military electronic equipment

explain, the hardware is not the problem: electronic component costs are not escalating greatly, but the cost of the software is. Already the results of this tendency have caused some hard decisions resulting in cancellation of projects, and no doubt compromises will be necessary in the future.

Conclusion

Chapter 1 described the inception and early work on radar which was given great impetus by the advent of the Second World War. This chapter has emphasised the continuing importance of radar as a military sensor and highlighted some exciting developments in radar techniques. Phased arrays and digital processing are currently having a major influence. The application of artificial intelligence (AI) is likely to be a further revolutionary step. Although the military need for radar is changing it is still undiminished. Surveillance sensors that can double up as verification devices is an important requirement. All this points to the conclusion that the military radar scene is one of a healthy and growing appetite fuelled by spectacular technical advances and tempered only by the escalating costs of this important technology.

Glossary of Terms and Abbreviations

A

Å	Angstrom (10^{-10} m)
AAA	Anti-aircraft artillery
Accuracy	Difference between measured and actual target position
AD	Air defence
Adaptive antenna	Antenna that automatically adjusts its radiation pattern to reduce interference or jamming (also null steering antennas)
AEW	Airborne early warning
AFV	Armoured fighting vehicle
AI	Artificial intelligence
Ambiguity	Gross error in measuring target position or speed
Amplitude fading	Periodic fading of radar signal due to target noise effects
Aperture	Area in front of antenna governing gain and beamwidth
ARM	Anti-radiation missile
ASPJ	Advanced self-protection jammer
ASTOR	Airborne/stand off radar
ASV	Airborne detection of surface vessels
AWACS	Airborne warning and control system
Azimuth	Angular measurement in horizontal plane

B

BMEWS	Ballistic missile early warning system
Beamwidth	Angular width of antenna beam at half power points
BITE	Built in test equipment
Bistatic radar	Radar with separated transmitter and receiver
Blind range	Radar range corresponding to time when next pulse is transmitted and hence when receiver is switched off
Blind speed	Target speed when target Doppler is same as PRF
B scope	Type of radar display
BSR	Battlefield surveillance radar

C

c	Velocity of light (3×10^8 m/s)
CAP	Combat air patrol. Operational procedure in which intercept aircraft loiter on station in the anticipated intercept area awaiting cuing on to target
Cassegrain antenna	Antenna with both main and sub-reflector
CEP	Circular error probable
CFAR	Constant false alarm rate
Chaff	Thin strips of metallised plastic deployed as cloud to provide a false target. Also called Window or Duppel
Clutter	Unwanted radar returns from ground, foliage, buildings, rain, etc
Clutter reference radar	Doppler radar using clutter return to extract target Doppler
CM	Countermeasures
Coaxial line	Microwave transmission line
COHO	Coherent oscillator
Conical scan	Tracking method using a rotating offset antenna beam
CP	Circular polarisation
CRO	Cathode ray oscilloscope
CRT	Cathode ray tube
CW	Continuous wave

D

dB	Decibel ($10 \log_{10}$ of parameter concerned)
DBS	Doppler beam sharpening
Doppler shift	Change in radar frequency upon reflection from moving target
Dump jammer	Expendable jammer delivered by aircraft, guns or missiles
Duppel	See Chaff
Duty Factor	Ratio of pulse repetition interval to pulse width

E

ECM	Electronic countermeasures. Any action intended to degrade the use of the EM spectrum by the enemy
ECCM	Electronic counter countermeasures. Action to oppose the enemy use of ECM
EIO	Extended interaction oscillator
ELINT	Electronic intelligence. The gathering of information about foreign use of EMR
EM	Electromagnetic
EMR	Electromagnetic radiation. General term for UV, visible

	light, IR, MMW, radar waves and radio waves of all wavelengths
E-O	Electro-optic
ERP	Effective radiated power. The product of the radiated power of a radar and its antenna gain on the direction of the receiver
ESM	Electronic support measures
EW	Electronic warfare. The conflict between two or more opponents over the use and denial of the EM spectrum

F

FAR	False alarm rate
FEBA	Forward edge of battle area
FET	Field effect transistor. A microwave generator or amplifier
FFT	Fast Fourier Transform
FMCW	Frequency modulated continuous wave transmission
FOFA	Follow-on forces attack
Foster scanner	Antenna giving rapid beam direction movement by rotating cone feed
Frequency agility	Rapid radar frequency change
Frequency scanning	Antenna technique to give rapid beam direction movement by frequency change

G

GaAs	Gallium arsenide, a material for microwave transistors and circuits
Gain (antenna)	Ratio of power radiated in main beam to that from a non-directive antenna
GCI	Ground controlled intercept
GHz	Gigahertz (10^9 Hz)
Glint	Movement of apparent target direction compared to its actual position
Gunn diode	Solid state microwave generator

H

Hot spot wander	Movement of apparent target position relative to its actual position
Hz	Hertz (cycle per second)

I

ICBM	Intercontinental ballistic missile
IF	Intermediate frequency
IFF	Identification, friend or foe
IMPATT	Impact avalanche transit time device; a solid state microwave generator

Internally coherent radar	Radar using internal signal to extract target Doppler
IR	Infra red. Electromagnetic radiation of wavelength longer than visible light
Isotropic	Antenna that radiates equally in all directions

K

kHz	Kilohertz (10^3 Hz)
Klystron	High power microwave tube generator or amplifier
Knot	Speed of one nautical mile per hour

L

LHCP	Left hand circular polarisation
LO	Local oscillator
LOAL	Lock on after launch (of a missile)
LOBL	Lock on before launch
LORO	Lobe on receive only (an ECM technique)
LOS	Line of sight
LP	Linear polarisation
LPI	Low probability of intercept
LWR	Laser warning receiving

M

Mach numbers	Velocity referred to the velocity of sound in air
Magnetron	High power microwave tube generator
MBT	Main battle tank
MHz	Megahertz (10^6 Hz)
MIC	Microwave integrated circuit
μs	Microsecond (10^{-6} s)
MLRS	Multiple launch rocket system
MW	Megawatt (10^6 W)
MMIC	Monolithic microwave integrated circuit
MMW	Millimetric wavelength electromagnetic radiation
Monopulse	Tracking method using four offset antenna beams or antenna with four quadrants
Monostatic radar	Radar transmitter and receiver co-located
MOPA	Master oscillator power amplifier. A form of transmitter
MTI	Moving target indication
Multiple beam antenna	Antenna with many simultaneous beams in different directions
Multistatic radar	Radar with many separated transmitters and receivers

N

Nato	North Atlantic Treaty Organisation
Nautical mile	Measure of distance equal to 6,080 ft

O

Offset reflector	Antenna in which feed is offset from aperture of main reflector to remove feed blockage

P

Phased array	Antenna comprising many elements each of whose phase is controlled to give rapid beam direction movement
PN	Proportional navigation. A form of missile guidance
PNC	Pseudo-noise code
PPI	Plan position indicator
PPS	Pulses per second
PRF	Pulse repetition frequency
Primary radar	Radar which detects target by reflected energy
Pulse compression	Reduction of pulse width on receive to enhance resolution

R

Radar	Radio detection and ranging
RAM	Radar absorbent material
RCS	Radar cross section (or scattering cross section or radar echoing area)
REA	Radar echoing area
Resolution	Ability to distinguish between two closely spaced targets
Resolution cell	Imaginary volume in space defined by angular and range resolutions
REW	Radar electronic warfare
RF	Radio frequency
RGS	Remote ground sensors
RGPO	Range gate pull off. A form of ECM
RHCP	Right hand circular polarisation
RPV	Remotely piloted vehicle. Usually airborne
RWR	Radar warning receiver. A form of ESM

S

SAGW	Surface-to-air guided weapon
SAM	Surface-to-air missile
SAR	Synthetic aperture radar
Secondary radar	Radar which detects target by signal returned from target borne transponder
Sidelobes	Antenna radiation or reception outside its main beam
SIJ	Stand in jammer

SLR	Sideways looking airborne radar
SLBM	Submarine launched ballistic missile
SLJ	Sidelobe jammer
SOJ	Stand off jammer
Sonde	A device sent into the atmosphere, often under a balloon or parachute, to obtain information about atmospheric conditions
SOR	Stand off radar
Spillover	Portion of power from antenna feed that does not hit reflector
SSR	Secondary surveillance radar
STA	Surveillance and target acquisition
Static split	Tracking using monopulse or other methods

T

TADR	Tank automatic defence radar
TBJ	Target borne jammer
TGM	Terminally guided munition
TGSM	Terminally guided sub-munition
TI	Thermal imaging
TOJ	Track on jam
Track while scan	Scanning radar that uses processing to extract target tracks
Twist Cassegrain	Antenna having both main and sub-reflector which uses polarisation twisting to remove sub-reflector blockage
TWT	Travelling wave tube. A high power microwave tube amplifier

U

UHF	Ultra-high frequency, 300–3,000 MHz
UMA	Unmanned aircraft
UMRV	Unmanned reconnaisance vehicle
UV	Ultra violet. Electromagnetic radiation of shorter wavelength than light

V

VDU	Visual display unit
VGPO	Velocity gate pull off

W

Waveguide	Rectangular metal tube used for transmission of microwaves
Window	See Chaff
WLR	Weapon locating radar

Bibliography

BROOKNER, E., *Radar Technology*, Artech House, Massachusetts, 1977.

EDWARDS, T. C., *Introduction to Microwave Electronics*, Edward Arnold, London, 1984.

GOLDEN, A., *Radar Electronic Warfare*, American Institute of Aeronautics and Astronautics Inc, New York, 1987.

International Countermeasures Handbook, EW Communications Inc, Palo Alto, California, published annually.

NATHANSON, F. E., *Radar Design Principles*, McGraw Hill, New York, 1969.

PELL, C., *Phased Array Radars*, Microwave Exhibitions and Publishers Ltd, UK, 1988.

RIDENOUR, L. N. and COLLINS, G. B. (editors), *Massachusetts Institute of Technology, Radiation Laboratory Series*, McGraw Hill, New York; 28 volumes including *Radar Systems Engineering* and others on radar topics.

SHERMON, S. M., *Monopulse Principles and Techniques*, Artech House, Massachusetts.

SKOLNIK, M. I., *Introduction to Radar Systems*, McGraw Hill, New York, 1980.

TOOMAY, J. C., *Radar Principles for the Non Specialist*, Lifetime Publications, California, 1982.

Index

Index